1988 IUCN RED LIST OF THREATENED ANIMALS

IUCN

IUCN (International Union for Conservation of Nature and Natural Resources) is a membership organisation comprising governments, non-governmental organisations (NGOs), research institutions, and conservation agencies, whose objective is to promote and encourage the protection and sustainable use of living resources.

Founded in 1948, IUCN has nearly 600 members representing 116 countries. Its six Commissions comprise a global network of experts on threatened species, protected areas, ecology, environmental planning, environmental law, and environmental education. Its thematic programmes include tropical forests, wetlands, marine ecosystems, plants, oceanic islands, the Sahel, Antarctica, and population and sustainable development.

THE IUCN CONSERVATION MONITORING CENTRE

The Conservation Monitoring Centre (CMC) is the division of IUCN that provides an information service to the Union, its members, and the conservation and development communities. CMC has developed an integrated and cross-referenced global database on animals, plants and habitats of conservation concern, on protected areas throughout the world, and on the international trade in wildlife species and products. CMC produces a wide variety of specialist outputs and reports based on the analysis of this data, including such major publications as the Red Data Books and Protected Areas Directories, which are now recognised as the authoritative reference works in their field.

Other IUCN Centres focus on Environmental Law, and Conservation for Development. Collectively, this information and expertise is used to assist IUCN and its members to develop conservation policy and implement programmes, and to promote a greater awareness of the need for sound conservation practice by the international development community.

Should you wish to consult these services please contact:

IUCN Secretariat, World Conservation Centre
Avenue du Mont-Blanc, CH-1196 Gland, Switzerland

1988 IUCN RED LIST
OF THREATENED ANIMALS

Prepared by

The IUCN Conservation Monitoring Centre
Cambridge U.K.

In association with the
International Council for Bird Preservation

With the support of the
David Shepherd Charitable Foundation

Guest Essay by

Dr Bruce Wilcox
Director, Center for Conservation Biology
Stanford University, California

International Union for Conservation of Nature
and Natural Resources

1988

Published by IUCN, Gland, Switzerland, and Cambridge, U.K.

Prepared with financial support from the World Wide Fund for Nature and the United Nations Environment Programme, and published with a grant from The David Shepherd Charitable Foundation.

A contribution to GEMS - the Global Environment Monitoring System.

ISBN: 2-88032-935-3

Printed by: Unwin Brothers, The Gresham Press, Old Woking, Surrey

Cover picture: Black Rhinos by David Shepherd kindly donated by the David Shepherd Charitable Foundation.

Available from: IUCN Publications Services,
219c Huntingdon Road, Cambridge, CB3 0DL, U.K.
or Avenue du Mont-Blanc, CH-1196 Gland, Switzerland

CONTENTS

PREAMBLE

The activities of the Species Survival Commission (SSC) and the Conservation Monitoring Centre (CMC) can be judged by their success in terms of species saved from extinction.

As we all know, there are many success stories that we can point to, but the sad reality is that we are still losing species every day as the relentless pressure from humankind continues.

If we do not develop a successful model in which population is stabilised we are all working in vain. Sustainable natural resources are limited, a message that we must ensure is fully understood.

Once one realises that between the covers of this deceptively slim volume we only have listed those species where we know the actual situation in the "wild", can one understand the possible stress and potential threat the majority of unlisted species - because of our lack of knowledge - are subjected to.

The aims for both the Species Survival Commission and the Conservation Monitoring Centre must be to obtain action for these listed species, which is where the forthoming SSC Action Plans play their role and, equally vitally, to ensure the steady build up and maintenance of the database for all the "conservationally" unknown species which we need to include in our concerns.

It is good to see this new 1988 edition of the IUCN Red List of Threatened Animals, and to thank the David Shepherd Charitable Foundation for their financial support in ensuring its publication. The hard work of all the CMC team carried out quietly and often under great financial stringency is again well rewarded in the quality of the publication.

Gren Ll. Lucas

Chairman,
IUCN Species Survival Commission

7 December 1987

INTRODUCTION

The IUCN Red List of Threatened Animals is an index of those animal species known to IUCN to be threatened with extinction. It complements the IUCN Red Data Book series, which contains detailed information on the status of species and of the measures needed to conserve them. Such information provides the essential first step in the development of action plans to conserve species, and in the development of priorities for scarce conservation funds. It also provides an information source for scientists, educationalists, zoos, the media and the general public, and is an important tool for the implementation of international wildlife treaties such as the Convention on International Trade in Endangered Species of Wild Flora and Fauna (CITES), the Bonn Migratory Species Convention, and the Convention on the Conservation of European Wildlife and Natural Habitats.

Conservation data held on individual species can be analysed to determine sites of special conservation concern, to determine the percentage of species known to occur in protected areas and those for which habitat protection is still non-existent, and those requiring legal protection. Such analyses in turn stimulate conservation activities, the results of which are then fed back into the data system to determine new conservation priorities. The IUCN Conservation Monitoring Centre in collaboration with IUCN's Species Survival Commission and the International Council for Bird Preservation (ICBP) are maintaining and developing this important data base on the status of the world's species as an essential component of their conservation programmes.

IUCN's threatened species list is compiled and maintained by the IUCN Conservation Monitoring Centre with assistance from the International Council for Bird Preservation. It is published periodically. For each threatened taxon, the list provides the scientific name, English vernacular name (where known), IUCN category (for definitions see page xvii), and a brief description of the animal's distribution. This is followed by an index to the list based on the order, family and generic listing. Vernacular names for major groupings such as monkeys, parrots, and butterflies are also included.

Data upon which the listings are made are gathered from literature searches and from correspondence with specialists around the world, including those belonging to the Specialist Groups of IUCN's Species Survival Commission and the International Council for Bird Preservation. The majority of vertebrate listings are based on the IUCN Red Data Books and recommendations and documentation provided by IUCN and ICBP. For invertebrates, however, it must be stressed that the list is only provisional, since most species have not yet been subjected to the same review process as has been carried out for the vertebrate groups, apart from those listed in the IUCN Invertebrate Red Data Book and the Swallowtail Butterfly Red Data Book. Other invertebrate listings have been taken from correspondence and a number of published sources (noted on page xv).

The number of threatened animal taxa identified by IUCN is 4589, comprised of 555 mammals, 1073 birds, 186 reptiles, 54 amphibians, 596 fishes, and 2125 invertebrates. However, except for birds, for which ICBP/IUCN have now attempted a global review, these numbers represent only those taxa whose threatened status is known to IUCN; many, many more taxa, particularly invertebrates, are threatened, and becoming extinct every year undescribed and unknown to the scientific and conservation communities. Thus the number of threatened taxa identified by IUCN represents only the visible fraction of a much greater problem. The magnitude of this problem is discussed in detail by Bruce Wilcox in the "Guest Essay" included in this volume (page v).

The IUCN threatened species list is constantly under review; as new areas or taxonomic groups are surveyed, species may be listed or delisted or categories may change, for example, the status of sea turtle species is currently under review. Since it is not possible for all parts of the list to be reviewed simultaneously it is inevitable that some parts of the list are more up-to-date than others.

The need for new information is continuous and assistance in providing accurate data always welcome. An inventory report form is detailed on page xi and is a guide to the information required by IUCN and ICBP to assess the international conservation status of a species.

The present list undoubtedly includes a number of errors and omissions, but it is to be hoped that these will stimulate people to send new information to:

The Species Conservation Monitoring Unit
IUCN Conservation Monitoring Centre
219c Huntingdon Road
Cambridge CB3 ODL
United Kingdom

GUEST ESSAY

TROPICAL DEFORESTATION AND EXTINCTION

Bruce A. Wilcox

We are entering a period of Earth's history when the global environment is changing on a scale and with an intensity that has occurred only a few times during the nearly four billion-year span of the existence of life on Earth. In the past, such changes were brought about by, for example, gradual tectonic movements in which entire continents repeatedly divided and coalesced, effecting global geographical and climatic conditions. Such changes are credited with the mass extinction of the world's shallow water marine organisms at the end of the Permian. Environmental changes also on a similar scale, but more abrupt, may have been precipitated by the impact of asteroids. One such event, producing a natural "nuclear winter," is postulated to have caused the extinction of the dinosaurs along with many lesser known organisms at the end of the Cretaceous. The present period of change, however, which will undoubtedly warrant its own geological epithet by future geologists, is being brought about neither by uncontrollable nor distant terrestrial or extraterrestrial forces, but by us.

This change is the result of the cumulative effects of over five billion human beings making a living on a planet of finite size and resources. As a consequence, particularly after a few hundred thousand years of cultural and technological advances, virtually all other forms of life are either being killed outright, slowly poisoned, or are being squeezed into smaller and smaller corners of the world - "protected areas" that are either purposely set aside, economically undesirable, inaccessible, or some combination of these.

To just grasp the dimensions of the environmental events that are unfolding, and their potential consequences, is perhaps well beyond our capacity. Yet at least some attempt to comprehend the causes and consequences is imperative if we are to avoid leaving a legacy of biotic annihilation that will outlast our own species.

But how does one measure and assess the long-term impacts of such changes as those apparently occurring on the level of global atmospheric fluxes of carbon dioxide and ozone? What about the "megaharvesting" of whales or of their resource base, krill, in the world's oceans, and the impact on the world's marine ecosystems? And, how about the capacity of both the marine and terrestrial ecosystems to absorb toxic wastes of every possible description? Finally, what about the wholesale destruction of entire ecosystems such as tropical forests and the impact on the vast number of species they support?

By all indications, each of these changes will seriously impact Earth's biota, and some may even precipitate another episode of mass extinction. The effects of one of them, destruction of the world's tropical forests, specifically has been so implicated. As their destruction is so obviously apparent and there richness so great, the consequences, as measured by the loss of thousands or millions of species in the foreseeable future is at least potentially comprehensible. A detailed look at tropical moist forests, their rate of destruction and disturbance, and how this may contribute to the global rate of endangerment and extinction, gives at least one measure of the magnitude of the current global environmental change taking place.

Broadly speaking, tropical forests include all forest formations in the tropical regions of the world, some of which are ecologically and structurally temperate. Excepting these, forests of the warm and at least seasonally humid environments still comprise an extremely heterogeneous group, including both dry and moist forests. The latter ranges from seasonally wet "monsoon forest" to true, more or less continuously wet "rain forest," which together constitute "tropical moist forest." Even these designations are insufficient and often generate confusion, some of which can be avoided by limiting general discussion of the statistics of forest disturbance to "closed broadleaved tropical forest" as designated by FAO. These, include all but a few percent of the total tropical moist cover in the world. The extent, rates, and kinds of disturbance of tropical forests have been most recently examined in detail by FAO (Lanly 1982).

On the IUCN Biogeographic Provinces map developed by Udvardy (1975) tropical moist forest (TMF) generally relates to those provinces labelled "tropical rain forest" and "tropical monsoon forest" as well as many of those labelled "tropical mixed island systems" and "tropical montane provinces with complex zonation." In theory, these once may have covered about 1600 million hectares, an amount thought to have existed prior to their extensive alteration by humans. By the mid-1970's TMF is estimated to have been reduced to approximately 1000 million hectares of intact ("primary") forest. About 400 million hectares had been "transformed" in roughly equal amounts to logged forest or shifting cultivation, and the remainder entirely lost (permanently cleared) for agriculture, grazing lands, various kinds of plantations, and other land uses.

The distinction between primary forest, disturbed forest (logged or that in shifting cultivation), and permanently cleared is critical to assessing the long-term consequences of deforestation or disturbance for two reasons. First, disturbance will not necessarily result in extinction, particularly if it is light and primary forest remains nearby. Second, given enough time, disturbed forest can regenerate and become primary forest. Unfortunately, at the present time not only is primary forest being permanently cleared, but a large fraction of that which is initially disturbed temporarily for logging or shifting cultivation is subsequently being permanently cleared. In addition, a significant fraction of the forest in the shifting cultivation cycle is effectively cleared permanently due to shortening the fallow period and exhaustion of the soil.

Key to projecting disturbance and loss of forest into the future, and in turn, endangerment and extinction of species, are estimates of the rates of transition from one category to the next. We must know, for example, the amount of primary forest transformed annually to logged forest, the amount of logged forest permanently cleared, etc. Thus, the total rate of loss or disturbance of forest and the amount in each category is computed by adding the rates of these different pathways. Rough estimates of these transition rates are provided by the FAO, filling in some of the gaps with figures reported in a study by the U. S. National Academy of Sciences (Myers 1980). Although in theory the pathways are bidirectional, increases in forest cover which counter the global trend of TMF destruction can be disregarded. The amount of increase due to regeneration or reforestation is insignificant compared to the current rates of disturbance and clearing.

The estimated worldwide rate of disturbance of primary forest and the rate of clearance of previously disturbed forest are both just under one percent annually. This does not include forest which is permanently lost directly from clearing of primary forest, or that left permanently unproductive due to over-cultivation of forest in shifting cultivation, fuelwood gathering, and numerous other factors affecting already disturbed forest that are difficult to monitor. The actual rate of permanent clearing is probably a little over one percent and combining disturbance and clearing, could be over two percent annually. This means that all TMF potentially could be disturbed or cleared in 50 years.

In fact, conservative estimates of the absolute annual amounts of forest conversion for the period from 1976 to 1980, for example, indicate that of the approximately 1200 million hectares of forest standing (primary or logged) in 1976, a minimum of 200 million hectares will have been cleared, and another 200 million will have been disturbed, by the turn of the century. This does not take into consideration the probable linkage of these rates to population growth, which is projected to continue in the tropical developing countries well into the middle of the next century. Thus, easily one-third of the forest remaining at the beginning of the last quarter of this century will have been disturbed or destroyed by the end of the century - just 12 years from now. Attempting predictions of global TMF losses beyond this is highly problematic and is quite academic at this point.

Deforestation is not of course equally distributed throughout the tropics. A number of areas are being disturbed so rapidly that virtually no undisturbed forest will remain outside the relatively few protected areas within the next few years. These so-called "hotspots" of deforestation include the moist forests of the Brazilian Atlantic coast, Columbian and Ecuadorian coasts, and those of Mexico, Central America, Australia, Indonesia, Indochina, Sri Lanka, Philippines, East and West Africa, and Madagascar.

Most of these forests will be completely disturbed in less than thirty years, and some, particularly in Central America and West Africa, are already virtually gone. The only significant blocks of relatively undisturbed forest that will be left by the middle of the next century will be in the Amazon and Zaire Basins and in northern South America (Guyana and Surinam).

Certainly, an assault of this magnitude will have profound consequences to the global pool of species, not to mention the effects on Earth's atmosphere and climate. There have been several attempts to estimate the rate of species extinction resulting from tropical deforestation. Because of the crudeness of such estimates, resulting not from ineptness but our ignorance of certain factors, these have met with everything from skepticism to outright hostility. In an attempt to produce at least a reasonably defensible assessment of the severity of the problem, several colleagues and I have been examining the approaches to making such estimates. Our goal is to at least identify the major impediments to obtaining a better assessment of the situation, if not to at least produce estimates to which levels of confidence can be attached.

The first serious impediment to estimating rates of species extinction is not knowing how many species there are in either tropical forests, or in the world as a whole. To begin with, something over 1.7 million species have been scientifically described. About 1.5 million of these are from the temperate regions, immediately suggesting that the tropics are extremely under represented due to the relative paucity of tropical collections and taxonomists working on them. We can guess at how under represented they are by looking at those groups that are relatively well studied in both regions, such as birds, mammals, and plants. In these taxa, about twice as many species occur in the tropics than temperate regions. Assuming that this ratio is constant among all taxa, there must be at least 3 million species in the tropics alone. The consensus among systematists therefore is that are at least 3 to 5 million species in the world. Add to this, however, the consideration that perhaps only half of the species that exist in the temperate and marine habitats have been discovered and described, and the number could be closer to 10 million.

It is doubtful, however, that the 2 to 1 ratio holds for all taxa. Invertebrates in particular, which constitute more than 95% of all described species, are generally thought to be especially rich in tropical forests. Butterflies, for example, the only major insect taxa that can be considered sufficiently well known to allow a tropical-temperate comparison suggest the ratio might be closer to 10 to 1. Thus, could there be 30 million species in the tropics? This is in fact the precise number recently estimated for insects alone in tropical moist forests based on studies of the canopy insect faunas in the Neotropics (Erwin 1982). This upward revision of the number of species in the world by ten-fold certainly is unsettling and further illustrates the difficulty in estimating global extinction rates.

There are at least two additional major problems in translating projected rates of forest disturbance and clearing into rates of endangerment and extinction. The first is figuring out what proportion of the tropical forest biota is unaffected by disturbance versus that which is affected. The second is relating the amount of forest affected by disturbance or clearing to species endangerment or extinction. These are both extremely complex problems that cannot be merely waved away. They represent perhaps the most significant technical challenges to protecting tropical diversity.

I shall not attempt to address the first problem except very briefly. The few existing studies relevant to the topic indicate that the effects of disturbance can range from virtually none to massive local reductions in species richness. For example, careful selective logging can leave the species composition of forest completely intact. On the other hand, intensive shifting cultivation, in which no primary forest remains in the vicinity, may literally decimate the biota of a forest.

The second problem is solved in theory by employing the "species-area relationship." This model, which is the mainstay of island biogeography, is best described for insular systems by "Darlington's rule" which states that reduction in the size of an area by a factor of ten, reduces the number of species by two. Applying the estimates of the amount of forest remaining by the year 2000, whether primary or disturbed, to this model (in its algebraic form) suggests that six or seven percent of all TMF species in the world are at risk and about three or four percent will be extinguished outright. Adding disturbance might contribute a few more percent to these categories.

As with all ecological models, which of course are always mere abstractions of nature, application of the species-area relationship entails certain critical assumptions. In this case the critical assumption is that species richness or habitat loss, or both, are evenly distributed geographically. In fact, the tendency for smaller areas to support fewer species is only a general one; some areas are extremely rich while others are impoverished despite their size. The validity of the above prediction thus assumes that on average both rich as well as impoverished forests are cleared indiscriminately.

A way around this assumption, and in fact, avoiding the species-area model altogether, is simply to focus on biota within definable areas certain to be completely cleared or disturbed by a particular date. My colleagues and I have done this by effectively superimposing the distributions of bird and mammal species on areas within those "hotspots" listed above to determine which species' ranges are entirely encompassed. We went a step further and eliminated all but those species endemic to the region. The result indicates that about nine percent of the world's birds and mammals are at high risk. We cannot say what proportion will disappear because of the lack of more detailed data on the amount of forest remaining in different disturbed states, and what fraction of the avian and mammalian faunas are affected by each state. While certainly only a fraction of the nine percent will go extinct, this estimate is only for a limited area of the total TMF.

We can attempt yet one more approach to estimating global TMF endangerment and extinction, which can serve as an independent check. Raven (personal communication) estimates that about 120,000 species of flowering plants, out of a world total of 250,000, occur in TMF regions that are certain to be either entirely cleared or disturbed in the next thirty years -- essentially most of the same forest areas listed above. In fact, at least a third of these species occur in the forests of only three countries: Columbia, Ecuador, and Peru. Gentry (1986) reports the recent clearing of a single ridge top in western Ecuador that resulted in the disappearance of as many as ninety plant species known only from that location -- an event that is occurring repeatedly.

Raven further suggests that flowering plants constitute about 1 in 10 to 1 in 20 of all species, assuming there are 5 to 10 million. So if one also considers that regions of highest plant diversity tend also to reflect the highest species diversity in general, on the order of 2.4 to 4.8 million species occur in these areas. If one further assumes that all but ten percent of the forest area remains reasonably undisturbed, then, following Darlington's rule, and acknowledging the critical assumptions we are making in applying the species-area model, half of these species will ultimate go extinct. Refining the calculation to consider the fraction of species that are on average immediately affected, roughly 30% will disappear during this time, which amounts to three-quarters of a million species, or 15% to 30% of all species.

Taken together, the three different approaches for predicting rates of global TMF extinction indicate that at least several hundred vertebrates, hundreds of thousands of plants, and over a million species of insects are endangered and will go extinct within the next three to five decades.

The argument is frequently made that extinction is natural and, as Darwin pointed out, unless the numbers go on increasing indefinitely, we must assume that extinction occurs at a rate matching that of the appearance of new species. Darwin's point was of course with reference to evolutionary time. Fossil evidence in fact confirms that 99% of the species that ever existed are now extinct. Our venue is that of the span of an individual human lifetime, since in fact, the extinctions just described will take place while most us are still living.

Even the previous mass extinction episodes were spread out over a much longer time period, at least millenniums, but upwards of millions of years. Actually, the present onslaught may well have begun with the mass extinction of Pleistocene mammals followed by a second prehistoric wave of human-caused extinctions occurring on many of the world's islands.

Today, islands remain the historic centers of endangerment and extinction, where, for example over 90% of the recorded avian extinctions have occurred. Until the present, however, the recorded extinction rate for higher vertebrates has been kept at a respectable 151 species over the past 400 years. This compares to a background rate, based on fossil evidence, of about one species every 50 to 100 years. When the tropical moist forest tallies start coming in, the documented extinctions will undoubtedly take another order of magnitude jump over the historic rate. Tragically, however, for every species listed as endangered or extinct at least a hundred more will probably disappear unrecorded.

DR BRUCE A. WILCOX, DIRECTOR
Center for Conservation Biology
Stanford University
Stanford, California 94305

References

- Erwin, T.L. (1982). Tropical forests: their richness in Coleoptera and other species. *Coleopt. Bull.* 36: 74-75.
- Gentry, A.W. (1986). Endemism in tropical versus temperate plant communities. In: M.E. Soule (Ed.), *Conservation Biology: the Science of Scarcity and Diversity.* Pp. 153-181. Sinauer Associates, Sunderland, Mass.
- Lanly, J.P. (1982). Tropical Forest Resources. FAO Paper #30. FAO Rome, Italy. 106pp.
- Myers, N. (1980). *Conversion of Tropical Moist Forests.* National Academy of Sciences, Washington, D.C., U.S.A.
- Udvardy, M.D.F. (1975). A classification of the biogeographical provinces of the world. *IUCN Occasional Paper* no. 18.

INVENTORY REPORT FORM

Report to be mailed to:
SCMU, IUCN Conservation Monitoring Centre
219(c) Huntingdon Rd, Cambridge, CB3 ODL, U.K.

1. Country

2. Date

3. Reporter

   Name: Address:

4. Taxon

   Scientific Name: Common Name:

5. Distribution

   Present: Former:

   If possible, please include a map. Is present range preferred or enforced habitat?

6. Population

   Estimated numbers in the wild. Indicate date of estimate and describe method of estimation. Are numbers increasing, decreasing or stable?

7. Habitat and Ecology

   Biome type. Elevation range. Brief notes about social structure, feeding habits and diet, reproduction (gestation, breeding season, number of young, age of sexual maturation), longevity etc.

8. Scientific interest and potential value

   Use in scientific or medical research; commercial value in trade or local economy.

9. Threats to Survival

   Eg. habitat destruction, over-exploitation, hybridization, natural disasters, competition for food.

10. Conservation Measures Taken

    Legal measures (international conventions, national laws); is law enforced? Protected areas - does it occur in national parks, reserves etc.? If so, please list. Management programmes or research programmes in progress.

11. Conservation Measures Proposed

    Same as for 10, but measures that are needed for the conservation of the taxon.

12. Captive Breeding

    Numbers in captivity. Does it breed readily in captivity? Where and when?

13. Remarks

Reference citations for description of animal. Comments about related taxa. If the above information concerns a subspecies then brief information should be given about the distribution and status of the species as a whole. Special acknowledgements etc.

14. References

Can be published papers, unpublished manuscripts, or references to correspondence (cited as *In litt.*).

DOCUMENTS ON WHICH THE IUCN RED LIST IS BASED

In addition, recommendations and documentation for listings have been provided by the IUCN/SSC Specialist Groups, and by ICBP.

The asterisk indicates books currently available from IUCN.

Mammals

- Goodwin, H.A. and Holloway, C.W. (1972). *Red Data Book, Vol. 1 - Mammalia.* Second Edition. IUCN, Morges. (Revisions: 1973 and 1974 by Goodwin, H.A. and Holloway, C.W.; 1976 by Fitter, R.S.R. and Holloway, C.W.; and 1978 by Thornback, J.).
- Thornback, J. and Jenkins, M. (1982). Terrestrial Mammals. Part VII. In: Threatened Species of Wild Flora and Vertebrate Fauna. Report to the Commission of the European Communities. The Nature Conservancy Council, Great Britain.
- Thornback, J. (1984). Wild Cattle, Bison and Buffaloes; their status and potential value. Report to UNEP. IUCN Conservation Monitoring Centre.
- *Thornback, J. and Jenkins, M. (1982). *The IUCN Mammal Red Data Book. Part 1. The Americas and Australasia.* IUCN, Gland.

Birds

- King, W.B. (1981). *Endangered Birds of the World. The ICBP Bird Red Data Book.* Smithsonian Institution Press and ICBP, Washington D.C.
- *Collar, N.J. and Andrew, P. (in prep.). Annotated Checklist of the Threatened Birds of the World. ICBP.
- *Collar, N.J. and Stuart, S.N. (1985). *Threatened Birds of Africa and Related Islands. The ICBP/IUCN Red Data Book, Part 1.* Third Edition. ICBP and IUCN, Cambridge.

Amphibians and Reptiles

- *Groombridge, B. (1982). *The IUCN Amphibia-Reptilia Red Data Book. Part 1, Testudines, Crocodylia, Rhynchocephalia.* IUCN, Gland.
- Groombridge, B. (1982). Amphibians and Reptiles. Part IV. In: Threatened Species of Wild Flora and Vertebrate Fauna. Report to the Commission of the European Communities. The Nature Conservancy Council, Great Britain.
- Honneger, R. (1975/1979). *Red Data Book, Vol. 3 - Amphibia and Reptilia.* Second Edition. IUCN, Gland.

Fishes

- *Evans, D. (1981). *Threatened Fish of Sri Lanka.* IUCN Conservation Monitoring Centre, Cambridge.
- Evans, D. and Almada-Villela, P. (Unpublished). Threatened Fishes of North America. Draft Document. IUCN Conservation Monitoring Centre.
- Harris, J.H. (Ed.) (1987). Proceedings of the Conference on Australian Threatened Fishes. Australian Society for Fish Biology. Melbourne 15-16 August 1985. Division of Fisheries, Department of Agriculture New South Wales. Sydney. 70 pp.
- Michaelis, F.B. (1985). Threatened fish. A Report on the threatened fish of inland waters in Australia. Australian National Parks and Wildlife Service Report 3. 45 pp.
- Miller, R.R. (1977). *Red Data Book, Vol. 4 - Pisces.* Second Edition. IUCN, Morges.

- Skelton, P.H. (1987). *South African Red Data Book Fishes.* South African National Scientific Programmes Report 137. 19 pp.
- U.S. Department of the Interior (1986). Endangered and Threatened Wildlife and Plants. *Federal Register* 50 CFR 17.11 and 17.12: 1-30

Invertebrates

- *Collins, N.M. and Morris, M.G. (1985). *Threatened Swallowtail Butterflies of the World. The IUCN Red Data Book.* IUCN, Gland and Cambridge.
- Collins, N.M. and Wells, S.M. (1986). Insects and other Invertebrates as Candidates for the Berne Convention. A Report to the Council of Europe. IUCN Conservation Monitoring Centre.
- IUCN/SSC Mollusc Specialist Group (1987). Action Plan for Molluscan Conservation: 1988-1992. 32 pp.
- U.S. Department of the Interior. (1984). Endangered and Threatened Wildlife and Plants; Review of Invertebrate Wildlife for Listing as Endangered or Threatened Species. *Federal Register* 49(100): 21664-21675.
- *Wells, S.M., Pyle, R.M. and Collins, N.M. (1983). *The IUCN Invertebrate Red Data Book.* IUCN, Gland.

TAXONOMY

The systems of classification and nomenclature principally follow the undermentioned authors.

Mammals

- Cabrera, A. (1957-61). Catalogo de los mamiferos de America del Sur. *Rev. del Mus. Argent. de Cienc. Nat. 'Bernardino Rivadavia' Cienc. Zool.* 4(1,2): 1-732.
- Corbet, G.B. and Hill, J.E. (1980). *A World List of Mammalian Species.* British Museum (Natural History) and Cornell University Press.
- Hall, E.R. and Kelson, K.R. (1959) *The Mammals of North America.* Ronald Press Co., New York.
- Honacki, J.H., Kinman, K.E. and Koeppl, J.W. (1982). *Mammal Species of the World: a taxonomic and geographic reference.* Allen Press Inc. and the Association of Systematics Collections, Kansas.
- Lovari, S. (1987). Evolutionary aspects of the biology of chamois, Rupicapra spp. (Bovidae, Caprinae). In: Soma, H. (ed.), *The Biology and Management of Capricornis and related Mountain Antelopes.* Croom Helm, London. Pp 51-61.
- Meester, J. and Setzer, H.W. (Eds) (1971). *The Mammals of Africa: an Identification Manual.* Smithsonian Institution Press, City of Washington.
- Ride, W.D.L. (1970). *A Guide to the Native Mammals of Australia.* Oxford University Press, Melbourne.

Birds

- Morony, J.J., Bock, W.J. and Farrand, J. (1975). *Reference List of the Birds of the World.* American Museum of Natural History, New York.

Reptiles

- Groombridge, B. (1988). *World Checklist of Threatened Amphibians and Reptiles.* Fourth Edition (in press). Nature Conservancy Council, Peterborough.
- Iverson, J.B. (1986). *A Checklist with Distribution Maps of the Turtles of the World.* Privately Printed. Paust Printing, Richmond, Indiana.
- Wermuth, H. and Mertens, R. (1977). Testudines, Crocodylia, Rhynchocephalia. *Das Tierreich* 100: 1-174.

Amphibians

- Frost, D.T. (1985). *Amphibian species of the world: A taxonomic and geographical reference.* Allen Press and the Association of Systematics Collections, Lawrence, Kansas. I-V, 1-732.

Fishes

- Greenwood, P.H. (1979). Towards a phyletic classification of the "genus" *Haplochromis* (Pisces, Cichlidae) and related taxa. Part 1. *Bulletin of the British Museum (Natural History) Zoology Series* 35(4): 265-322.
- Nelson, J.S. (1984). *Fishes of the World.* Second Edition. John Wiley and Sons, New York, Chichester, Brisbane, Toronto, Singapore.
- Parenti, L.R. (1981). A phylogenetic and biogeographic analysis of cyprinodontiform fishes (Teleostei, Atherinomorpha). *Bulletin of the American Museum of Natural History* 168(4): 335-557.
- Robins, C.R., Bailey, R.M., Bond, C.E., Brooker, J.R., Lachner, E.A., Lea, R.N., Scott, W.B. (1980). *A List of Common and Scientific Names of Fishes from the United States and Canada.* Fourth Edition. American Fisheries Society Special Publication No. 12.

° Rosen, D.E. and Parenti, L.R. (1981). Relationships of *Oryzias* and the groups of Atherinomorph fishes. *American Museum Novitates* 2719: 1-25.
° Trewavas, E. (1983). *Tilapiine fishes of the genera Sarotherodon, Oreochromis and Danakilae.* British Museum (Natural History), London. 583 pp.

Invertebrates

° Hancock, D.L. (1983). Classification of the Papilionidae (Lepidoptera): a phylogenetic approach. *Smithersia* 2: 1-48.
° Parker, S.B. (1982). *Synopsis and Classification of Living Organisms.* McGraw-Hill, New York.

IUCN THREATENED SPECIES CATEGORIES

Species identified as threatened by IUCN are assigned a category indicating the degree of threat. Definitions are as follows:

EXTINCT (Ex)

Species not definitely located in the wild during the past 50 years (criterion as used by the Convention on International Trade in Endangered Species of Wild Fauna and Flora).

N.B. On a few occasions, the category Ex? has been assigned; this denotes that it is virtually certain that the taxon has recently become extinct.

ENDANGERED (E)

Taxa in danger of extinction and whose survival is unlikely if the causal factors continue operating.

Included are taxa whose numbers have been reduced to a critical level or whose habitats have been so drastically reduced that they are deemed to be in immediate danger of extinction. Also included are taxa that may be extinct but have definitely been seen in the wild in the past 50 years.

VULNERABLE (V)

Taxa believed likely to move into the 'Endangered' category in the near future if the causal factors continue operating.

Included are taxa of which most or all the populations are decreasing because of over-exploitation, extensive destruction of habitat or other environmental disturbance; taxa with populations that have been seriously depleted and whose ultimate security has not yet been assured; and taxa with populations that are still abundant but are under threat from severe adverse factors throughout their range.

N.B. In practice, 'Endangered' and 'Vulnerable' categories may include, temporarily, taxa whose populations are beginning to recover as a result of remedial action, but whose recovery is insufficient to justify their transfer to another category.

RARE (R)

Taxa with small world populations that are not at present 'Endangered' or 'Vulnerable', but are at risk.

These taxa are usually localised within restricted geographical areas or habitats or are thinly scattered over a more extensive range.

INDETERMINATE (I)

Taxa *known* to be 'Endangered', 'Vulnerable' or 'Rare' but where there is not enough information to say which of the three categories is appropriate.

INSUFFICIENTLY KNOWN (K)

Taxa that are *suspected* but not definitely known to belong to any of the above categories, because of lack of information.

K* Taxa which are currently under review by ICBP and which are likely to be designated a category in the near future.

THREATENED (T)

Threatened is a general term to denote species which are 'Endangered', 'Vulnerable', 'Rare', 'Indeterminate', or 'Insufficiently Known' and should not be confused with the use of the same term by the U.S. Office of Endangered Species. In this volume it is used to identify taxa comprised of several sub-taxa which have differing status categories.

COMMERCIALLY THREATENED (CT)

Taxa not currently threatened with extinction, but most or all of whose populations are threatened as a sustainable commercial resource, or will become so, unless their exploitation is regulated.

This category applies only to taxa whose populations are assumed to be relatively large.

N.B. In practise, this category has only been used for marine species of commercial importance that are being overfished in several parts of their ranges.

ABBREVIATIONS

Arch.	Archipelago
Eq. Guinea	Equatorial Guinea
F.R.G.	Federal Republic of Germany
I.	Island
Is	Islands
O.	Ocean
sp.	Unnamed species
U.A.E.	United Arab Emirates
U.K.	United Kingdom
U.S.A.	United States of America
U.S.S.R.	Union of Soviet Socialist Republics
[]	Former Distribution
*	An important, introduced population

1988 IUCN RED LIST
OF THREATENED ANIMALS

MAMMALS

Phylum CHORDATA

Class MAMMALIA

Order MONOTREMATA			
Family Tachyglossidae			
Zaglossus bruijni	Long-beaked Echidna	V	New Guinea
Order MARSUPIALIA			
Family Macropodidae			
Bettongia lesueur	Burrowing Bettong	R	Australia
Bettongia penicillata	Brush-tailed Bettong	E	Australia
Caloprymnus campestris	Desert Rat-kangaroo	I	Australia
Dendrolagus dorianus notatus	Doria's Tree-kangaroo	V	New Guinea
Dendrolagus goodfellowi shawmayeri	Goodfellow's Tree-kangaroo	V	Papua New Guinea
Dorcopsis atrata	Black Dorcopsis Wallaby	R	Papua New Guinea
Dorcopsulus macleayi	Papuan Dorcopsis	R	Papua New Guinea
Lagorchestes asomatus	Central Hare-wallaby	Ex	[Australia]
Lagorchestes hirsutus	Rufous Hare-wallaby	R	Australia
Lagorchestes leporides	Eastern Hare-wallaby	Ex	[Australia]
Lagostrophus fasciatus	Banded Hare-wallaby	R	Australia
Macropus greyi	Toolache Wallaby	Ex	[Australia]
Onychogalea fraenata	Bridled Nailtail Wallaby	E	Australia
Onychogalea lunata	Crescent Nailtail Wallaby	Ex	[Australia]
Petrogale persephone	Proserpine Rock-wallaby	R	Australia
Potorous longipes	Long-footed Potoroo	I	Australia
Potorous platyops	Broad-faced Potoroo	Ex	[Australia]
Family Phalangeridae			
Phalanger lullulae	Woodlark Island Cuscus	E	Woodlark I.(Papua New Guinea)
Phalanger rufoniger	Black-spotted Cuscus	R	New Guinea
Phalanger permixtio	Cuscus	R	Papua New Guinea
Phalanger vestitus	Cuscus	R	New Guinea
Family Petauridae			
Gymnobelideus leadbeateri	Leadbeater's Possum	V	Australia
Family Vombatidae			
Lasiorhinus krefftii	Northern Hairy-nosed Wombat	E	Australia

Family Peramelidae			
Chaeropus ecaudatus	Pig-footed Bandicoot	Ex	[Australia]
Echymipera clara	White-lipped Bandicoot	R	New Guinea
Perameles bougainville	Western Barred Bandicoot	R	Australia
Perameles eremiana	Desert Bandicoot	Ex	[Australia]
Family Thylacomyidae			
Macrotis lagotis	Greater Bilby	E	Australia
Macrotis leucura	Lesser Bilby	Ex	[Australia]
Family Dasyuridae			
Antechinus apicalis	Dibbler	I	Australia
Phascogale calura	Red-tailed Phascogale	I	Australia
Sminthopsis douglasi	Julia Creek Dunnart	I	Australia
Sminthopsis longicaudata	Long-tailed Dunnart	K	Australia
Sminthopsis psammophila	Sandhill Dunnart	K	Australia
Family Myrmecobiidae			
Myrmecobius fasciatus	Numbat	E	Australia
Family Thylacinidae			
Thylacinus cynocephalus	Thylacine	Ex	[Australia]
Order INSECTIVORA			
Family Solenodontidae			
Solenodon cubanus	Cuban Solenodon	E	Cuba
Solenodon paradoxus	Haitian Solenodon	E	Hispaniola
Family Tenrecidae			
Geogale aurita aurita	Large-eared Tenrec	K	Madagascar
Geogale aurita orientalis	Eastern Large-eared Tenrec	I	Madagascar
Limnogale mergulus	Web-footed Tenrec	V	Madagascar
Microgale brevicaudata		K	Madagascar
Microgale crassipes		K	Madagascar
Microgale drouhardi		K	Madagascar
Microgale longicaudata		K	Madagascar
Microgale longirostris		K	Madagascar
Microgale majori		K	Madagascar
Microgale melanorrhachis		K	Madagascar
Microgale occidentalis		I	Madagascar

Microgale parvula		K	Madagascar
Microgale principula		K	Madagascar
Microgale prolixicaudata		K	Madagascar
Microgale sorella		K	Madagascar
Microgale taiva		K	Madagascar
Microgale thomasi		K	Madagascar
Microgale (Leptogale) gracilis		K	Madagascar
Family Chrysochloridae			
Amblysomus gunningi	Gunning's Golden Mole	K	South Africa
Amblysomus julianae	Juliana's Golden Mole	R	South Africa
Chlorotalpa duthiae	Duthie's Golden Mole	R	South Africa
Chrysochloris visagiei	Visagie's Golden Mole	K	South Africa
Chrysospalax trevelyani	Giant Golden Mole	E	South Africa
Chrysospalax villosus	Rough-haired Golden Mole	K	South Africa
Cryptochloris wintoni	De Winton's Golden Mole	K	South Africa
Cryptochloris zyli	Van Zyl's Golden Mole	K	South Africa
Family Erinaceidae			
Podogymnura truei	Mindanao Gymnure	V	Philippines
Family Soricidae			
Crocidura maquassiensis	Maquassie Musk Shrew	R	South Africa, Zimbabwe
Myosorex longicaudatus		R	South Africa
Family Talpidae			
Desmana moschata	Russian Desman	V	U.S.S.R.
Galemys pyrenaicus	Pyrenean Desman	V	France, Portugal, Spain
Order CHIROPTERA			
Family Pteropodidae			
Acerodon lucifer	Panay Giant Fruit Bat	Ex	[Panay I.(Philippines)]
Alionycteris paucidentata		K	Mindanao (Philippines)
Aproteles bulmerai		K	E.New Guinea
Dobsonia exoleta chapmani	Chapman's Fruit Bat	Ex?	[Negros I.(Philippines)]
Dobsonia minor	Lesser Naked-backed Fruit Bat	K	Irian Jaya
Dyacopterus brooksi		K	Sumatra
Dyacopterus spadicens	Dayak Fruit Bat	K	Malaya, Borneo
Latidens salimalii		K	S.India

Species	Common name	Status	Distribution
Megaerops kusnotoi	Javan Tail-less Fruit Bat	K	Java
Nyctimene rabori	Philippines Tube-nosed Fruit Bat	E	Negros I. (Philippines)
Otopteropus cartilagonodus		K	Luzon (Philippines)
Pteropus insularis	Carolines Flying Fox	I	C.Caroline Is
Pteropus livingstonii	Comoro Black Flying Fox	E	Comoro Is
Pteropus macrotis	Big-eared Flying Fox	I	New Guinea, Aru Is
Pteropus mariannus	Marianas Flying Fox	V	Mariana Is, Palau Is, Caroline Is, Ryukyu Is (Japan)
Pteropus molossinus		I	E.Caroline Is
Pteropus niger	Mauritian Flying Fox	V	Mauritius
Pteropus phaeocephalus		I	Truck Is (C.Caroline Is)
Pteropus pilosus	Palau Flying Fox	Ex	[Palau I.]
Pteropus rodricensis	Rodrigues Flying Fox	E	Rodrigues
Pteropus samoensis	Samoan Flying Fox	E	Samoa, Fiji Is
Pteropus seychellenis aldabrensis	Seychelles Flying Fox	V	Aldabra I. (Seychelles)
Pteropus subniger		Ex	[Mauritius, Reunion]
Pteropus tokudae	Guam Flying Fox	Ex	[Guam]
Pteropus tonganus	Insular Flying Fox	I	N.E.New Guinea, Samoa, Cook Is
Pteropus voeltzkowi	Pemba Flying Fox	V	Pemba I.(Tanzania)
Family Emballonuridae			
Emballonura furax	Greater Sheath-tailed Bat	K	New Guinea
Emballonura raffrayana	Raffray's Sheath-tailed Bat	K	Seram I., New Guinea, Solomons
Coleura seychellensis	Seychelles Sheath-tailed Bat	E	Seychelles
Family Craseonycteridae			
Craseonycteris thonglongyai	Kitti's Hog-nosed Bat	R	Thailand
Family Megadermatidae			
Macroderma gigas	Ghost Bat	V	N.Australia
Family Hipposideridae			
Hipposideros papua	Geelvinck Bay Leaf-nosed Bat	R	Biak I.(Irian Jaya)
Hipposideros ridleyi	Ridley's Leaf-nosed Bat	I	Singapore, Pen. Malaysia, Sabah
Rhinonicteris auranta	Orange Leaf-nosed Bat	K	N.Australia
Family Phyllostomidae			
Leptonycteris nivalis	Mexican Long-nosed Bat	V	S.U.S.A. to Guatemala
Leptonycteris yerbabuenae		V	S.U.S.A. to El Salvador

Phyllonycteris aphylla	Jamaican Flower Bat	K	Jamaica
Phyllonycteris major	Puerto Rican Flower Bat	Ex?	[Puerto Rico]
Phyllonycteris poeyi	Cuban Flower Bat	K	Cuba, Hispaniola
Family Myzopodidae			
Myzopoda aurita	Sucker-footed Bat	K	Madagascar
Family Vespertilionidae			
Glischropus javanus	Javan Thick-thumbed Bat	K	Java
Kerivoula africana	Tanzanian Woolly Bat	Ex?	[Tanzania]
Lasiurus cinereus semotus	Hawaiian Hoary Bat	I	Hawaii (U.S.A.)
Myotis bartelsii	Bartel's Myotis	K	Java
Myotis capaccinii	Long-fingered Bat	V	Europe,S.Asia Minor, N.W.Africa
Myotis dasycneme	Pond Bat	K	Europe to W.Siberia
Myotis grisescens	Grey Bat	E	U.S.A.
Myotis hermani	Herman's Myotis	R	N.W.Sumatra
Myotis myotis	Mouse-eared Bat	K	Europe to Ukraine
Myotis sodalis	Indiana Bat	V	U.S.A.
Plecotus townsendii	Townsend's Big-eared Bat	I	U.S.A.
Family Mystacinidae			
Mystacina robusta	New Zealand Lesser Short-tailed Bat	Ex	[New Zealand]
Mystacina tuberculata	New Zealand Greater Short-tailed Bat	V	New Zealand
Family Molossidae			
Otomops formosus	Javan Mastiff Bat	K	Java
Order PRIMATES			
Family Lemuridae			
Hapalemur griseus	Grey Gentle Lemur	K	Madagascar
Hapalemur simus	Broad-nosed Gentle Lemur	E	Madagascar
Hapalemur sp. nova	Golden Gentle Lemur	I	Madagasgar
Lemur catta	Ring-tailed Lemur	K	Madagascar
Lemur coronatus	Crowned Lemur	K	Madagascar
Lemur macaco flavifrons	Sclater's Lemur	E	Madagascar
Lemur macaco macaco	Black Lemur	V	Madagascar
Lemur mongoz	Mongoose Lemur	V	Madagascar, Comoro Is
Lemur rubriventer	Red-bellied Lemur	I	Madagascar
Lepilemur dorsalis	Grey-backed Sportive Lemur	K	Madagascar

Lepilemur edwardsi	Milne-Edwards' Sportive Lemur	K	Madagascar
Lepilemur leucopus	White-footed Sportive Lemur	K	Madagascar
Lepilemur microdon	Microdon (?) Sportive Lemur	K	Madagascar
Lepilemur mustelinus	Weasel Lemur	K	Madagascar
Lepilemur ruficaudatus	Red-tailed Sportive Lemur	K	Madagascar
Lepilemur septentrionalis	Northern Sportive Lemur	K	Madagascar
Varecia variegata	Ruffed Lemur	I	Madagascar
Family Cheirogaleidae			
Allocebus trichotis	Hairy-eared Dwarf Lemur	E	Madagascar
Microcebus coquereli	Coquerel's Dwarf Lemur	R	Madagascar
Phaner furcifer	Fork-marked Lemur	K	Madagascar
Family Indridae			
Avahi laniger	Woolly Lemur	K	Madagascar
Indri indri	Indris	E	Madagascar
Propithecus diadema	Diademed Sifaka	V	Madagascar
Propithecus verreauxi	Verreaux's Sifaka	K	Madagascar
Family Daubentoniidae			
Daubentonia madagascariensis	Aye-aye	E	Madagascar
Family Lorisidae			
Arctocebus calabarensis	Angwantibo	K	West Africa
Nycticebus pygmaeus	Pygmy Loris	V	Indochina
Family Galagidae			
Galago thomasi	Thomas's Bushbaby	K	East Africa
Galago zanzibaricus	Zanzibar Bushbaby	K	East Africa
Family Tarsiidae			
Tarsius syrichta	Philippine Tarsier	E	Philippines
Tarsius pumilus	Lesser Spectral Tarsier	I	Sulawesi
Family Cebidae			
Alouatta fusca	Brown Howler Monkey	I	Bolivia, Brazil
Alouatta villosa	Guatemalan Black Howler Monkey	I	Belize, Guatemala, Mexico
Ateles belzebuth	Long-haired Spider Monkey	V	South America
Ateles fusciceps	Brown-headed Spider Monkey	I	Colombia, Ecuador, Panama
Ateles geoffroyi	Geoffroy's Spider Monkey	V	Central America, Mexico

Ateles paniscus	Black Spider Monkey	V	South America
Brachyteles arachnoides	Woolly Spider Monkey	E	Brazil
Cacajao calvus	Red & White Uakari	V	Brazil, Colombia, Peru
Cacajao melanocephalus	Black-headed Uakari	V	Brazil, Colombia, Venezuela
Callicebus personatus	Masked Titi	V	Brazil
Chiropotes albinasus	White-nosed Saki	V	Brazil
Chiropotes satanas satanas	Southern Bearded Saki	E	Brazil
Lagothrix flavicauda	Yellow-tailed Woolly Monkey	E	Ecuador, Peru
Lagothrix lagothricha	Woolly Monkey	V	South America
Saimiri oerstedi	Central American Squirrel Monkey	E	Costa Rica, Panama
Family Callitrichidae			
Callimico goeldii	Goeldi's Marmoset	R	South America
Callithrix argentata leucippe	White Marmoset	V	Brazil
Callithrix aurita	Buffy-tufted-ear Marmoset	E	Brazil
Callithrix flaviceps	Buffy-headed Marmoset	E	Brazil
Callithrix humeralifer	Tassel-eared Marmoset	V	Brazil
Leontopithecus rosalia	Golden Lion Tamarin	E	Brazil
Leontopithecus chrysomelas	Golden-headed Lion Tamarin	E	Brazil
Leontopithecus chrysopygus	Golden-rumped Lion Tamarin	E	Brazil
Saguinus bicolor	Bare-faced Tamarin	I	Brazil, Peru
Saguinus imperator	Emperor Tamarin	I	Bolivia, Brazil, Peru
Saguinus leucopus	White-footed Tamarin	V	Colombia
Saguinus oedipus oedipus	Cotton-top Tamarin	E	Colombia
Family Cercopithecidae			
Allenopithecus nigroviridis	Allen's Swamp Monkey	K	Congo, Zaire
Cercocebus aterrimus	Black Mangabey	K	N.Angola, C.Zaire
Cercocebus galeritus	Crested Mangabey	V	Kenya, Tanzania
Cercocebus galeritus galeritus	Tana River Mangabey	E	Kenya
Cercocebus torquatus	Collared Mangabey	V	West Africa
Cercopithecus diana	Diana Monkey	V	West Africa
Cercopithecus erythrogaster	White-throated Guenon	E	Benin, Nigeria
Cercopithecus erythrotis	Russet-eared Guenon	E	Cameroon, Bioko, Nigeria
Cercopithecus hamlyni	Owl-faced Guenon	V	Rwanda, Uganda, Zaire
Cercopithecus lhoesti	L'hoest's Monkey	V	Burundi, Rwanda, Uganda, Zaire
Cercopithecus preussi	Preuss's Guenon	E	Cameroon, Bioko, Nigeria
Cercopithecus salongo	Salongo Guenon	K	Zaire

Cercopithecus solatus	Sun-tailed Guenon	V	Gabon
Colobus satanas	Black Colobus	E	Cameroon, Congo, Eq. Guinea, Gabon
Procolobus [badius] badius	Western Red Colobus	V	West Africa
Procolobus [b.] badius waldroni	Miss Waldron's Bay Colobus	E	Ghana, Ivory Coast
Procolobus [badius] pennanti	Pennant's Red Colobus	E	Congo, Bioko, Cameroon
Procolobus [badius] rufomitratus	Peter's Red Colobus	V	East & C.Africa
Procolobus [b.]badius rufomitratus	Tana River Red Colobus	E	Kenya
Procolobus [badius] gordonorum	Uhehe Red Colobus	E	Tanzania
Procolobus [badius] kirkii	Zanzibar Red Colobus	E	Zanzibar
Procolobus verus	Olive Colobus	V	West Africa
Papio hamadryas	Hamadryas Baboon	R	Ethiopia, Somalia, S.Arabia
Mandrillus leucophaeus	Drill	E	Cameroon, Bioko, Nigeria
Mandrillus sphinx	Mandrill	V	Cameroon, Congo, Eq. Guinea, Gabon
Theropithecus gelada	Gelada	R	Ethiopia
Macaca brunnescens	Muna-Butung Macaque	K	Sulawesi
Macaca cyclopsis	Taiwan Macaque	V	Taiwan
Macaca hecki	Heck's Macaque	V	Sulawesi
Macaca maura	Moor Macaque	V	Sulawesi
Macaca pagensis	Mentawai Macaque	E	Mentawai Is (Indonesia)
Macaca silenus	Lion-tailed Macaque	E	S. India
Macaca sylvanus	Barbary Macaque	V	Algeria, Gibraltar*, Morocco
Macaca thibetana	Tibetan Macaque	K	China
Nasalis larvatus	Proboscis Monkey	V	Borneo
Presbytis comata	Javan Leaf Monkey	E	Java
Presbytis potenziani	Mentawai Leaf Monkey	E	Mentawai Is. (Indonesia)
Trachypithecus francoisi	Tonkin Leaf Monkey	E	Indochina, S.W.China
Trachypithecus leucocephalus	White-headed Black Leaf Monkey	E	S.China
Trachypithecus geei	Golden Leaf Monkey	R	Bhutan, India
Trachypithecus johnii	Nilgiri Leaf Monkey	E	S. India
Pygathrix nemaeus	Red-shanked Douc Monkey	E	C.Vietnam, E.C.Laos,
Pygathrix nigripes	Black-shanked Douc Monkey	E	S.Vietnam, S.Laos, E.Cambodia
Rhinopithecus avunculus	Tonkin Snub-nosed Monkey	E	N. Vietnam
Rhinopithecus bieti	Yunnan Snub-nosed Monkey	E	China
Rhinopithecus brelichi	Guizhou Snub-nosed Monkey	E	China
Rhinopithecus roxellanae	Sichuan Golden Snub-nosed Monkey	V	China
Simias concolor	Pig-tailed Langur	E	Mentawai Is (Indonesia)

(**Trachypithecus* now used for many previous *Presbytis*)*

Family Hylobatidae			
Hylobates concolor	Black Gibbon	V	China, Indochina
Hylobates hoolock	Hoolock Gibbon	V	Assam, Burma, Yunnan
Hylobates klossi	Kloss's Gibbon	E	Mentawai Is (Indonesia)
Hylobates moloch	Javan Gibbon	E	Java
Hylobates pileatus	Pileated Gibbon	V	Indochina, Thailand
Family Pongidae			
Gorilla gorilla	Gorilla	V	Equatorial Africa
Gorilla gorilla beringei	Mountain Gorilla	E	Rwanda, Uganda, Zaire
Gorilla gorilla graueri	Eastern Lowland Gorilla	E	E. Zaire
Pan paniscus	Pygmy Chimpanzee	V	Zaire
Pan troglodytes	Chimpanzee	V	Equatorial Africa
Pan troglodytes verus	West African Chimpanzee	E	West Africa
Pongo pygmaeus	Orang-utan	E	Borneo, Sumatra
Order EDENTATA			
Family Myrmecophagidae			
Myrmecophaga tridactyla	Giant Anteater	V	Central & South America
Family Bradypodidae			
Bradypus torquatus	Maned Sloth	E	Brazil
Family Dasypodidae			
Clamyphorus retusus	Burmeister's Armadillo	K	Argentina, Bolivia, Paraguay
Chlamyphorus truncatus	Pink Fairy Armadillo	K	Argentina
Priodontes giganteus	Giant Armadillo	V	South America
Tolypeutes tricinctus	Brazilian Three-banded Armadillo	I	Brazil
Order LAGOMORPHA			
Family Ochotonidae			
Prolagus sardus	Sardinian Pika	Ex	[Sardinia, Corsica]
Family Leporidae			
Bunolagus monticularis	Riverine Rabbit	E	South Africa
Caprolagus hispidus	Hispid Hare	E	Himalayan foothills
Lepus flavigularis	Tehuantepec Hare	E	Mexico
Nesolagus netscheri	Sumatran Short-eared Rabbit	I	Sumatra
Pentalagus furnessi	Amami Rabbit	E	Ryukyu Is (Japan)
Romerolagus diazi	Volcano Rabbit	E	Mexico

Order RODENTIA

Species	Common name	Status	Distribution
Family Aplodontidae			
Aplodontia rufa nigra	Point Arena Mountain Beaver	I	California (U.S.A.)
Aplodontia rufa phaea	Point Reyes Mountain Beaver	I	California (U.S.A.)
Family Sciuridae			
Cynomys parvidens	Utah Prairie Dog	V	U.S.A.
Marmota vancouverensis	Vancouver Island Marmot	E	Canada
Marmota menzbieri	Menzbier's Marmot	V	U.S.S.R.
Sciurus niger cinereus	Delmarva Fox Squirrel	E	U.S.A.
Syntheosciurus brochus	Mountain Squirrel	K	Costa Rica, Panama
Family Heteromyidae			
Dipodomys elator	Texas Kangaroo Rat	R	Texas (U.S.A.)
Dipodomys gravipes	San Quintin Kangaroo Rat	E	Baja California (Mexico)
Dipodomys heermanni morroensis	Morro Bay Kangaroo Rat	E	California (U.S.A.)
Dipodomys ingens	Giant Kangaroo Rat	I	California (U.S.A.)
Dipodomys nitratoides exilis	Fresno Kangaroo Rat	E	California (U.S.A.)
Dipodomys nitratoides nitratoides	Tipton Kangaroo Rat	E	California (U.S.A.)
Dipodomys stephensi	Stephens Kangaroo Rat	I	California (U.S.A.)
Perognathus alticola	White-eared Pocket Mouse	V	California (U.S.A.)
Perognathus inornatus psammophilus	Salinas Pocket Mouse	E	California (U.S.A.)
Perognathus longimembris brevinasus	Los Angeles Pocket Mouse	E	California (U.S.A.)
Family Cricetidae			
Neotoma fuscipes riparia	San Joaquin Valley Woodrat	V	California (U.S.A.)
Pitymys bavaricus	Bavarian Pine Vole	Ex	[F.R.G.]
Reithrodontomys megalotis limicola	Southern Marsh Harvest Mouse	V	California (U.S.A.)
Reithrodontomys raviventris	Salt-marsh Harvest Mouse	E	California (U.S.A.)
Sigmodon arizonae plenus	Colorado River Cotton Rat	E	California (U.S.A.)
Zapus trinotatus orarius	Point Reyes Jumping Mouse	I	California (U.S.A.)
Family Muridae			
Batomys granti	Luzon Forest Rat	I	Philippines
Conilurus albipes	Rabbit-eared Tree-rat	Ex	[Australia]
Leporillus apicalis	Lesser Stick-nest Rat	Ex	[Australia]
Leporillus conditor	Greater Stick-nest Rat	R	Australia
Microtus breweri	Beach Vole	R	U.S.A.
Microtus californicus scirpensis	Amargosa Vole	E	California (U.S.A.)

Notomys amplus	Short-tailed Hopping-mouse	Ex	[Australia]
Notomys aquilo	Northern Hopping-mouse	K	Australia
Notomys fuscus	Dusky Hopping-mouse	I	Australia
Notomys longicaudatus	Long-tailed Hopping-mouse	Ex	[Australia]
Notomys macrotis	Big-eared Hopping-mouse	Ex	[Australia]
Notomys mordax	Darling Downs Hopping-mouse	Ex	[Australia]
Oryzomys argentatus	Silver Rice Rat	I	U.S.A.
Pseudomys fieldi	Alice Springs Mouse	Ex	[Australia]
Pseudomys oralis	Hastings River Mouse	I	Australia
Pseudomys praeconis	Shark Bay Mouse	R	Australia
Tokudaia osimensis muenninki	Ryukyu Spiny Rat	I	Ryukyu Is
Xeromys myoides	False Water-rat	K	Australia
Zyzomys pedunculatus	Central Rock-rat	I	Australia
Family Erithizontidae			
Chaetomys subspinosus	Thin-spined Porcupine	I	Brazil
Family Chinchillidae			
Chinchilla brevicaudata	Short-tailed Chinchilla	I	Andes
Chinchilla lanigera	Long-tailed Chinchilla	I	Chile
Family Capromyidae			
Capromys angelcabrerai	Cabrera's Hutia	E	Cuba
Capromys auritus	Large-eared Hutia	E	Cuba
Capromys garridoi	Garrido's Hutia	I	Cuba
Capromys melanurus	Bushy-tailed Hutia	I	Cuba
Capromys nanus	Dwarf Hutia	E	Cuba
Capromys sanfelipensis	Little Earth Hutia	E	Cuba
Geocapromys brownii	Jamaican Hutia	I	Jamaica
Geocapromys ingrahami	Bahamian Hutia	R	Bahamas
Plagiodontia aedium	Hispaniolan Hutia	I	Hispaniola
Order CETACEA			
Family Iniidae			
Inia geoffrensis	Boto, Amazon River Dolphin	V	South America
Family Platanistidae			
Platanista gangetica	Ganges River Dolphin	V	India, Bangladesh, Nepal, Bhutan
Platanista minor	Indus River Dolphin	E	Pakistan

Family Pontoporiidae			
Lipotes vexillifer	Baiji, Yangtze River Dolphin	E	Yangtse R. (China)
Pontoporia blainvillei	Franciscana, La Plata Dolphin	K	Brazil, Uruguay, Argentina
Family Delphinidae			
Cephalorhynchus commersonii	Commerson's Dolphin	K	Coastal South Atlantic
Cephalorhynchus eutropia	Black Dolphin	K	Coastal Chile
Cephalorhynchus heavisidii	Heaviside's Dolphin	K	Coastal South Africa & Namibia
Cephalorhynchus hectori	Hector's Dolphin	K	Coastal New Zealand
Family Monodontidae			
Delphinapterus leucas	White Whale	K	Arctic & sub-Arctic Ocean
Monodon monoceros	Narwhal	K	Arctic Ocean
Orcaella brevirostris	Irrawaddy Dolphin	K	Rivers and coasts from Bay of Bengal to N.Australia
Family Phocoenidae			
Phocoena phocoena	Harbour Porpoise	K	Coastal waters of N.Hemisphere
Phocoena sinus	Vaquita	V	Gulf of California (Mexico)
Family Ziphiidae			
Hyperoodon ampullatus	Northern Bottlenose Whale	V	North Atlantic
Family Balaenopteridae			
Balaenoptera musculus	Blue Whale	E	All Oceans
Balaenoptera physalus	Fin Whale	V	All Oceans
Megaptera novaeangliae	Humpback Whale	E	All Oceans
Family Balaenidae			
Balaena mysticetus	Bowhead Whale	E	Arctic, N.Atlantic & N.Pacific Oceans
Eubalaena australis	Southern Right Whale	V	S. Atlantic, Pacific, Indian & Southern Oceans
Eubalaena glacialis	Northern Right Whale	E	N.Atlantic & N.Pacific Oceans
Order CARNIVORA			
Family Canidae			
Canis lupus	Grey Wolf	V	North America, Middle East, Eurasia
Canis rufus	Red Wolf	E	U.S.A.

Canis simensis	Simen Fox	E	Ethiopia
Chrysocyon brachyurus	Maned Wolf	V	South America
Cuon alpinus	Dhole	V	Asia
Dusicyon australis	Falkland Island Wolf	Ex	[Falkland Is]
Dusicyon microtis	Small-eared Zorro	K	South America
Lycaon pictus	African Wild Dog	V	Subsaharan Africa
Speothos venaticus	Bush Dog	V	South America
Vulpes bengalensis	Bengal Fox	K	India, Pakistan, S.Nepal
Family Ursidae			
Ailuropoda melanoleuca	Giant Panda	R	China
Melursus ursinus	Sloth Bear	I	India, Nepal, Sri Lanka
Selenarctos thibetanus gedrosianus	Baluchistan Bear	E	Iran, Pakistan
Tremarctos ornatus	Spectacled Bear	V	South America
Ursus arctos nelsoni	Mexican Grizzly Bear	Ex	[Mexico, U.S.A.]
Ursus maritimus	Polar Bear	V	Arctic
Family Procyonidae			
Ailurus fulgens	Red Panda	K	Nepal to China
Procyon gloveralleni	Barbados Racoon	Ex?	[Barbados]
Procyon pygmaeus	Cozumel Island Racoon	K	Cozumel I. (Mexico)
Nasua nelsoni	Cozumel Island Coati	K	Cozumel I. (Mexico)
Family Mustelidae			
Aonyx cinerea	Oriental Small-clawed Otter	K	Asia
Lutra felina	Marine Otter	V	Coastal Chile & Peru, [Argentina]
Lutra longicaudis longicaudis	La Plata Otter	V	South America
Lutra lutra lutra	European Otter	V	Eurasia
Lutra perspicillata	Smooth-coated Otter	K	Asia
Lutra provocax	Southern River Otter	V	W. Argentina, C.&S.Chile
Lutra sumatrana	Hairy-nosed Otter	K	South-east Asia
Pteronura brasiliensis	Giant Otter	V	South America
Conepatus mesoleucus telmalestes	Big Thicket Hog-nosed Skunk	I	E.Texas (U.S.A.)
Gulo gulo	Wolverine	V	Eurasia, North America
Martes flavigula chrysospila	Taiwan Yellow-throated Marten	I	Taiwan
Martes gwatkinsi	Nilgiri Marten	I	S.India
Martes melampus tsuensis	Tsushima Island Marten	I	Japan
Melogale everetti	Kinabalu Ferret-badger	K	Sabah
Melogale orientalis	Javan Ferret-badger	K	Java

Mustela lutreola	European Mink	V	Europe
Mustela lutreolina	Indonesian Mountain Weasel	K	Java, S.Sumatra?
Mustela nigripes	Black-footed Ferret	E	U.S.A.
Vormela peregusna peregusna	European Marbled Polecat	V	C.Europe to Greece & Turkey
Family Viverridae			
Arctogalidia trivirgata trilineata	Javan Small-toothed Palm Civet	I	Java
Chrotogale owstoni	Owston's Palm Civet	K	Indochina
Cryptoprocta ferox	Fossa	K	Madagascar
Cynogale bennettii	Otter civet	K	South-east Asia
Eupleres goudotii	Falanouc	V	Madagascar
Fossa fossana	Malagasy Civet	V	Madagascar
Genetta abyssinica	Abyssinian Genet	K	Ethiopia, N.Somalia
Genetta genetta isabelae	Ibiza Common Genet	R	Spain
Genetta johnstoni	Johnston's Genet	K	Liberia, Guinea
Macrogalidia musschenbroekii	Sulawesi Palm Civet	R	Sulawesi
Paradoxurus jerdoni	Jerdon's Palm Civet	I	S.India
Poiana richardsoni liberiensis	Leighton's Linsang	I	Liberia, Ivory Coast, Sierra Leone?
Viverra megaspila civettina	Malabar Large Spotted Civet	E	Western Ghats (India)
Family Herpestidae			
Bdeogale crassicauda omnivora	Sokoke Bushy-tailed Mongoose	E	N.Coastal Tanzania, Kenya
Bdeogale crassicauda tenuis	Zanzibar Bushy-tailed Mongoose	I	Zanzibar
Bdeogale jacksoni	Jackson's Mongoose	K	C.Kenya, S.E.Uganda
Galidictis grandidiensis	Giant-striped Mongoose	K	Madagascar
Galidictis fasciata	Malagasy Broad-striped Mongoose	I	Madagascar
Liberiictis kuhni	Liberian Mongoose	E	N.E.Liberia, Ivory Coast?, Guinea?
Mungotictis decemlineata	Malagasy Narrow-striped Mongoose	V	Madagascar
Salanoia concolor	Malagasy Brown-tailed Mongoose	K	Madagascar
Family Hyaenidae			
Hyaena brunnea	Brown Hyaena	V	Southern Africa
Hyaena hyaena barbara	Barbary Hyaena	E	Algeria, Morocco, Tunisia
Family Felidae			
Acinonyx jubatus	Cheetah	V	Africa, Middle East, Iran, U.S.S.R.
Acinonyx jubatus venaticus	Asiatic Cheetah	E	Iran, U.S.S.R.
Felis badia	Bornean Bay Cat	R	Borneo
Felis caracal michaelis	Turkmenian Caracal Lynx	R	U.S.S.R.

Felis concolor coryi	Florida Cougar	E	U.S.A.
Felis concolor cougar	Eastern Cougar	E	Canada, U.S.A.
Felis iriomotensis	Iriomote Cat	E	Ryukyu Is (Japan)
Felis jacobita	Andean Cat	R	Andes
Felis margarita scheffeli	Pakistan Sand Cat	E	Pakistan
Felis marmorata	Marbled Cat	I	Asia
Felis pardalis	Ocelot	V	U.S.A., Central & South America
Felis pardina	Pardel Lynx	E	Portugal, Spain
Felis planiceps	Flat-headed Cat	I	South-east Asia
Felis rubiginosa	Rusty-spotted Cat	K	India, Sri Lanka
Felis temmincki	Asiatic Golden Cat	I	Asia
Felis tigrina	Little Spotted Cat	V	Central & South America
Felis wiedii	Margay	V	Central & South America
Felis yagouaroundi	Jaguarundi	I	U.S.A., Central & South America
Neofelis nebulosa	Clouded Leopard	V	Asia
Panthera leo persica	Asiatic Lion	E	India
Panthera onca	Jaguar	V	U.S.A., Central & South America
Panthera pardus	Leopard	T	Africa, Middle East, Asia
Panthera tigris	Tiger	E	Asia
Panthera uncia	Snow Leopard	E	Asia
Family Otariidae			
Arctocephalus philippii	Juan Fernandez Fur Seal	V	Chile
Arctocephalus townsendi	Guadalupe Fur Seal	V	Mexico, U.S.A.
Zalophus californianus japonicus	Japanese Sea Lion	E	Japan, North & South Korea
Family Odobenidae			
Odobenus rosmarus laptevi	Laptev Walrus	K	U.S.S.R.
Family Phocidae			
Monachus monachus	Mediterranean Monk Seal	E	Mediterranean & Mauritanian coasts
Monachus schauinslandi	Hawaiian Monk Seal	E	Hawaii
Monachus tropicalis	Caribbean Monk Seal	Ex?	[Caribbean]
Phoca hispida saimensis	Saimaa Seal	E	Finland
Phoca vitulina stejnegeri	Kuril Seal	V	Kuril Sea
Order PROBOSCIDEA			
Family Elephantidae			
Elephas maximus	Asian Elephant	E	Asia
Loxodonta africana	African Elephant	V	Africa

Order SIRENIA			
Family Dugongidae			
Dugong dugon	Dugong	V	Coastal Indian & Western Pacific Oceans
Hydrodamalis gigas	Steller's Sea Cow	Ex	[Bering Sea, North Pacific Ocean]
Family Trichechidae			
Trichechus inunguis	Amazonian Manatee	V	Amazon basin
Trichechus manatus	West Indian Manatee	V	Caribbean & South American Coasts & Rivers
Trichechus senegalensis	West African Manatee	V	West Africa
Order PERISSODACTYLA			
Family Equidae			
Equus africanus	African Wild Ass	E	North-east Africa
Equus grevyi	Grevy's Zebra	E	Ethiopia, Kenya, [Somalia]
Equus hemionus	Asiatic Wild Ass	V	Asia
Equus hemionus hemippus	Syrian Wild Ass	Ex	[Syria]
Equus hemionus khur	Indian Wild Ass	E	Pakistan, India
Equus przewalskii	Przewalski's Horse	Ex?	[China, Mongolia]
Equus quagga quagga	True Quagga	Ex	[South Africa]
Equus zebra hartmannae	Hartmann's Mountain Zebra	V	Angola, Namibia
Equus zebra zebra	Cape Mountain Zebra	E	South Africa
Family Tapiridae			
Tapirus bairdii	Central American Tapir	V	Central & North-west South America
Tapirus indicus	Malayan Tapir	E	South-east Asia
Tapirus pinchaque	Mountain Tapir	V	North-west South America
Family Rhinocerotidae			
Ceratotherium simum cottoni	Northern Square-lipped Rhinoceros	E	Zaire, S.Sudan
Diceros bicornis	Black Rhinoceros	E	Africa
Didermocerus sumatrensis	Sumatran Rhinoceros	E	South-east Asia
Rhinoceros sondaicus	Javan Rhinoceros	E	Java
Rhinoceros unicornis	Great Indian Rhinoceros	E	India, Nepal

Order ARTIODACTYLA

Species	Common name	Status	Distribution
Family Suidae			
Babyrousa babyrussa	Babirusa	V	Sulawesi, Buru, Sulu & Togian Is
Sus barbatus cebifrons	Visayan Warty Pig	V	Visayan Is (Philippines)
Sus barbatus oi	Western Bearded Pig	V	Malaysia, Indonesia
Sus salvanius	Pygmy Hog	E	[Bangladesh], India, Nepal
Sus scrofa riukiuanus	Ryukyu Islands' Wild Pig	V	Ryukyu Is (Japan)
Sus verrucosus	Javan and Bawean Warty Pigs	V	Java & Bawean I.
Family Tayassuidae			
Catagonus wagneri	Chacoan Peccary	V	Argentina, Bolivia, Paraguay
Family Hippopotamidae			
Choeropsis liberiensis	Pygmy Hippopotamus	V	West Africa
Family Camelidae			
Camelus bactrianus	Wild Bactrian Camel	V	China, Mongolia
Vicugna vicugna	Vicuna	V	Andes
Family Cervidae			
Axis calamianensis	Calamian Deer	V	Calamian I. (Philippines)
Axis kuhli	Kuhl's Deer	R	Bawean I. (Indonesia)
Blastocerus dichotomus	Marsh Deer	V	Central South America
Cervus albirostris	Thorold's Deer	I	China
Cervus alfredi	Visayan Spotted Deer	E	Visayan Is (Philippines)
Cervus duvauceli	Swamp Deer	E	India, Nepal
Cervus elaphus bactrianus	Bactrian Deer	E	Afghanistan, U.S.S.R.
Cervus elaphus barbarus	Barbary Deer	V	Algeria, Tunisia
Cervus elaphus corsicanus	Corsican Red Deer	E	[Corsica], Sardinia
Cervus elaphus hanglu	Hangul	E	India
Cervus elaphus macneilli	M'Neill's Deer	I	China
Cervus elaphus wallichi	Shou	E	China, Bhutan
Cervus elaphus yarkandensis	Yarkand Deer	E	China
Cervus eldi eldi	Manipur Brow-antlered Deer	E	India
Cervus eldi siamensis	Thailand Brow-antlered Deer	E	South-east Asia
Cervus nippon grassianus	Shansi Sika	E	China
Cervus nippon keramae	Ryukyu Sika	E	Ryukyu Is
Cervus nippon kopschi	South China Sika	E	China
Cervus nippon mandarinus	North China Sika	E	China

Cervus nippon taiouanus	Formosan Sika	E	Taiwan
Dama mesopotamica	Persian Fallow Deer	E	Mesopotamia
Hippocamelus antisensis	North Andean Huemul	V	North Andes
Hippocamelus bisulcus	South Andean Huemul	E	South Andes
Moschus chrysogaster (subspecies)	Himalayan subspecies of Musk Deer	V	Himalayas
Muntiacus crinifrons	Black Muntjac	I	China
Muntiacus feae	Fea's Muntjac	E	Burma, Thailand
Odocoileus hemionus cerrosensis	Cedros Island Mule Deer	R	Mexico
Odocoileus virginianus clavium	Key Deer	R	U.S.A.
Ozotoceros bezoarticus celer	Argentinian Pampas Deer	E	Argentina
Pudu mephistophiles	Northern Pudu	I	Andes
Family Antilocapridae			
Antilocapra americana peninsularis	Lower California Pronghorn	E	Mexico
Antilocapra americana sonoriensis	Sonoran Pronghorn	E	Mexico, U.S.A.
Family Bovidae			
Bison bonasus	European Bison	V	U.S.S.R., Poland
Bos gaurus	Gaur	V	South-east Asia
Bos grunniens	Wild Yak	E	Central Asia
Bos javanicus	Banteng	V	South-east Asia
Bos sauveli	Kouprey	E	Indochina
Bubalus bubalis	Wild Asiatic Water Buffalo	E	India, Nepal
Bubalus depressicornis	Lowland Anoa	E	Sulawesi
Bubalus mindorensis	Tamaraw	E	Philippines
Bubalus quarlesi	Mountain Anoa	E	Sulawesi
Taurotragus derbianus derbianus	Western Giant Eland	E	West Africa
Addax nasomaculatus	Addax	E	Sahara/Sahel
Aepyceros melampus petersi	Black-faced Impala	E	Angola, Namibia
Alcelaphus buselaphus swaynei	Swayne's Hartebeest	E	Ethiopia, Somalia
Alcelaphus buselaphus tora	Tora Hartebeest	E	Egypt, Ethiopia, Sudan
Ammodorcas clarkei	Dibatag	V	Ethiopia, Somalia
Cephalophus adersi	Ader's Duiker	V	Kenya, Tanzania, Zanzibar
Cephalophus jentinki	Jentink's Duiker	E	Ivory Coast, Liberia
Cephalophus spadix	Abbott's Duiker	V	Tanzania
Cephalophus zebra	Zebra Duiker	V	Ivory Coast, Liberia, Sierra Leone
Damaliscus dorcas dorcas	Bontebok	V	South Africa
Damaliscus hunteri	Hunter's Antelope	R	Kenya, Somalia, Tanzania
Dorcatragus megalotis	Beira Antelope	K	Djibouti, Ethiopia, Somalia

Gazella cuvieri	Cuvier's Gazelle	E	North-west Africa
Gazella dama	Dama Gazelle	V	Sahara/Sahel
Gazella dorcas	Dorcas Gazelle	V	Sahara/Sahel & Middle East
Gazella gazella	Mountain Gazelle	V	Arabia, Middle East
Gazella leptoceros	Slender-horned Gazelle	V	Sahara/Sahel
Gazella rufifrons	Red-fronted Gazelle	V	Senegal to Eritrea
Gazella soemmerringi	Soemmerring's Gazelle	V	North-eastern Africa
Gazella spekei	Speke's Gazelle	V	Somalia, Ethiopia
Gazella subgutturosa marica	Saudi Goitred Gazelle	E	Arabia
Hippotragus leucophaeus	Bluebuck	Ex	[South Africa]
Hippotragus niger variani	Giant Sable Antelope	E	Angola
Kobus leche	Lechwe	V	Southern Africa
Neotragus moschatus moschatus	Zanzibar Suni	E	Zanzibar
Oryx dammah	Scimitar-horned Oryx	E	Sahara/Sahel
Oryx leucoryx	Arabian Oryx	E	Arabia, Middle East
Tragelaphus buxtoni	Mountain Nyala	E	Ethiopia
Capricornis crispus swinhoei	Formosan Serow	V	Taiwan
Capricornis sumatraensis sumatraensis	Sumatran Serow	E	Sumatra
Budorcas taxicolor bedfordi	Golden Takin	R	China
Budorcas taxicolor tibetana	Szechwan Takin	I	China
Nemorhaedus baileyi	Red Goral	V	Burma, India, China
Hemitragus hylocrius	Nilgiri Tahr	V	India
Hemitragus jayakari	Arabian Tahr	E	Oman, U.A.E.
Capra falconeri	Markhor	V	West Himalayas
Capra falconeri megaceros	Straight-horned Markhor	E	Afghanistan, Pakistan
Capra pyrenaica pyrenaica	Pyrenean Ibex	E	Spain
Capra walie	Walia Ibex	E	Ethiopia
Rupicapra rupicapra cartusiana	Chartreuse Chamois	E	France
Rupicapra rupicapra tatrica	Tatra Chamois	R	Czechoslovakia, Poland
Rupicapra pyrenaica ornata	Abruzzo Chamois	V	Italy
Ammotragus lervia	Barbary Sheep	V	Sahara/Sahel
Ovis ammon	Argali	I	Mtns of C.Asia
Ovis orientalis musimon	Sardinian Mouflon	V	Sardinia, Corsica
Ovis orientalis ophion	Cyprus Mouflon	V	Cyprus

BIRDS

CLASS AVES

Species	Common name	Status	Distribution
Order APTERYGIFORMES			
Family Apterygidae			
Apteryx owenii	Little Spotted Kiwi	K*	New Zealand
Order TINAMIFORMES			
Family Tinamidae			
Tinamus solitarius	Solitary Tinamou	K*	Argentina, Brazil, Paraguay
Tinamus osgoodi	Black Tinamou	K*	Colombia, Peru
Crypturellus saltuarius	Magdalena Tinamou	I	Colombia
Crypturellus noctivagus	Yellow-legged Tinamou	K*	Brazil
Crypturellus transfasciatus	Pale-browed Tinamou	K*	Ecuador, Peru
Nothoprocta taczanowskii	Taczanowski's Tinamou	K*	Peru
Nothoprocta kalinowskii	Kalinowski's Tinamou	K*	Peru
Nothura minor	Lesser Nothura	K*	Brazil
Taoniscus nanus	Dwarf Tinamou	K*	Argentina, Brazil
Order SPHENISCIFORMES			
Family Speniscidae			
Megadyptes antipodes	Yellow-eyed Penguin	K*	New Zealand
Spheniscus demersus	Jackass Penguin	S	Namibia, South Africa
Spheniscus humboldti	Peruvian Penguin	K*	Chile, Peru
Order PODICIPEDIFORMES			
Family Podicipedidae			
Tachybaptus pelzelni	Madagascar Little Grebe	K	Madagascar
Tachybaptus rufolavatus	Alaotra Grebe	E	Madagascar
Podilymbus gigas	Atitlan Grebe	Ex	Guatemala
Podiceps andinus	Colombian Grebe	Ex	Colombia
Podiceps taczanowskii	Junin Grebe	E	Peru
Podiceps gallardoi	Hooded Grebe	R	Argentina
Order PROCELLARIIFORMES			
Family Diomedeidae			
Diomedea amsterdamensis	Amsterdam Albatross	E	Amsterdam I. (France)
Diomedea albatrus	Short-tailed Albatross	E	Japan

Family Procellariidae			
Pterodroma aterrima	Mascarene Black Petrel	E	Mauritius
Pterodroma feae	Gon-gon	R	Cape Verde Is, Madeira (Portugal)
Pterodroma madeira	Freira	E	Madeira (Portugal)
Pterodroma hasitata	Black-capped Petrel	V	Cuba, Dominican Republic, Haiti
Pterodroma cahow	Cahow	E	Bermuda
Pterodroma becki	Beck's Petrel	I	Papua New Guinea, Solomon Is
Pterodroma ultima	Murphy's Petrel	K*	Pitcairn Is (U.K.), Tuamotu Archipelago (France), Tubuai Is (France)
Pterodroma magentae	Magenta Petrel	E	Chatham Is (New Zealand)
Pterodroma phaeopygia	Dark-rumped Petrel	E	Galapagos (Ecuador), Hawaiian Is (U.S.A.)
Pterodroma cooki	Cook's Petrel	K*	New Zealand
Pterodroma axillaris	Chatham Island Petrel	E	Chatham Is (New Zealand)
Pterodroma defilippiana	Defilippe's Petrel	K*	Chile
Pterodroma pycrofti	Pycroft's Petrel	K*	New Zealand
Pterodroma macgillivrayi	Fiji Petrel	I	Fiji
Procellaria parkinsoni	Black Petrel	E	New Zealand
Procellaria westlandica	Westland Black Petrel	V	New Zealand
Puffinus creatopus	Pink-footed Shearwater	K*	Juan Fernandez Is (Chile)
Puffinus heinrothi	Heinroth's Shearwater	I	Papua New Guinea
Puffinus newelli	Newell's Shearwater	K*	Hawaiian Is (USA)
Puffinus auricularis	Townsend's Shearwater	K*	Mexico
Family Hydrobatidae			
Oceanodroma macrodactyla	Guadalupe Storm-petrel	Ex	Mexico
Oceanodroma markhami	Markham's Storm-petrel	K*	Eastern Pacific Ocean
Oceanodroma tristrami	Sooty Storm-petrel	K*	Hawaiian Is (U.S.A.), Japan
Oceanodroma hornbyi	Ringed Storm-petrel	K*	Chile, Ecuador, Peru
Family Pelecanoididae			
Pelecanoides garnoti	Peruvian Diving Petrel	K*	Chile, Peru
Order PELECANIFORMES			
Family Pelecanidae			
Pelicanus crispus	Dalmatian Pelican	V	Western Palearctic
Pelecanus philippensis	Spot-billed Pelican	K*	Burma, China, India, Indonesia, Kampuchea, Laos, Malaysia, Thailand, Viet Nam

Family Sulidae			
Sula abbotti	Abbott's Booby	E	Christmas I. (Australia)
Family Phalacrocoracidae			
Phalacrocorax carunculatus	New Zealand King Cormorant	K*	New Zealand
Phalacrocorax pygmeus	Pygmy Cormorant	K*	Western Palearctic
Nannopterum harrisi	Galapagos Flightless Cormorant	R	Galapagos (Ecuador)
Family Fregatidae			
Fregata aquila	Ascension Frigatebird	R	Ascension I. (U.K.)
Fregata andrewsi	Christmas Frigatebird	V	Christmas I. (Australia)
Order CICONIIFORMES			
Family Ardeidae			
Ixobrychus novaezelandia	New Zealand Little Bittern	K*	New Zealand
Gorsachius goisagi	Japanese Night-heron	K*	China, Indonesia, Japan, Philippines, Taiwan
Gorsachius magnificus	White-eared Night-heron	K*	China
Egretta vinaceigula	Slaty Egret	I	Botswana, Namibia, Zambia
Egretta eulophotes	Chinese Egret	V	China, Indonesia, Malaysia, North Korea, Philippines
Ardea humbloti	Madagascar Heron	K	Madagascar, Comoros
Ardea imperialis	White-bellied Heron	K*	Bhutan, Burma, India, Nepal
Family Balaenicipitidae			
Balaeniceps rex	Shoebill	S	Central and East Africa
Family Ciconiidae			
Mycteria cinerea	Milky Stork	V	Indonesia, Kampuchea, Malaysia, Viet Nam
Ciconia stormi	Storm's Stork	I	Indonesia, Malaysia, Thailand
Ciconia boyciana	Oriental White Stork	E	China, Japan, South Korea, U.S.S.R.
Leptoptilos dubius	Greater Adjutant	K*	Bangladesh, Burma, India, Kampuchea, Laos, Thailand, Viet Nam
Family Threskiornithidae			
Pseudibis davisoni	White-shouldered Ibis	I	Burma, Indonesia, Kampuchea, Laos, Thailand, Viet Nam
Pseudibis gigantea	Giant Ibis	R	Kampuchea, Laos, Thailand, Viet Nam
Geronticus eremita	Northern Bald Ibis	E	North-west Africa, Turkey, Ethiopia, North Yemen

Geronticus calvus	Southern Bald Ibis	R	Lesotho, South Africa, Swaziland
Nipponia nippon	Crested Ibis	E	China, Japan
Bostrychia bocagei	Dwarf Olive Ibis	I	Sao Tomé
Platalea minor	Black-faced Spoonbill	K*	China, Japan, North Korea, Philippines, Taiwan, Viet Nam
Family Phoenicopteridae			
Phoenicoparrus andinus	Andean Flamingo	K*	Argentina, Bolivia, Chile, Peru
Phoenicoparrus jamesi	Puna Flamingo	K*	Argentina, Bolivia, Chile, Peru
Order ANSERIFORMES			
Family Anhimidae			
Chauna chavaria	Northern Screamer	K*	Colombia, Venezuela
Family Anatidae			
Dendrocygna arborea	West Indian Whistling-duck	V	Caribbean Islands
Anser erythropus	Lesser White-fronted Goose	K*	Western Palearctic
Branta sandvicensis	Hawaiian Goose	V	Hawaiian Is (U.S.A.)
Stictonetta naevosa	Freckled Duck	K*	Australia
Tadorna cristata	Crested Shelduck	K*	South Korea, U.S.S.R.
Cairina scutulata	White-winged Duck	V	Bangladesh, Burma, India, Indonesia, Thailand
Aix galericulata	Mandarin Duck	K*	China, Japan, North Korea, South Korea, Taiwan, U.S.S.R.
Anas formosa	Baikal Teal	K*	China, Japan, North Korea, South Korea, U.S.S.R
Anas bernieri	Madagascar Teal	V	Madagascar
Anas aucklandica	New Zealand Brown Teal	V	New Zealand
Marmaronetta angustirostris	Marbled Teal	K*	Western Palearctic
Rhodonessa caryophyllacea	Pink-headed Duck	Ex	India, Nepal
Aythya innotata	Madagascar Pochard	E	Madagascar
Mergus octosetaceus	Brazilian Merganser	I	Argentina, Brazil, Paraguay
Mergus squamatus	Scaly-sided Merganser	I	China, U.S.S.R.
Mergus australis	Auckland Island Merganser	Ex	New Zealand
Oxyura leucocephala	White-headed Duck	K*	Western Palearctic

Species	Common name	Status	Distribution
Order FALCONIFORMES			
Family Cathartidae			
Gymnogyps californianus	California Condor	E	U.S.A.
Family Accipitridae			
Chondrohierax wilsonii	Cuban Kite	R	Cuba
Henicopernis infuscata	Black Honey Buzzard	K*	Papua New Guinea
Milvus milvus	Red Kite	K*	Western Palearctic
Haliaeetus vociferoides	Madagascar Fish-eagle	E	Madagascar
Haliaeetus leucoryphus	Pallas's Fish-eagle	K*	Burma, China, India, Iran, Pakistan, U.S.S.R.
Haliaeetus albicilla	White-tailed Fish-eagle	V	Palearctic
Haliaeetus pelagicus	Steller's Fish-eagle	K*	Japan, Korea, U.S.S.R.
Gyps coprotheres	Cape Vulture	R	Southern Africa
Aegypius monachus	Black (Cinereous) Vulture	K*	Palearctic
Spilornis klossi	Nicobar Serpent-eagle	K*	Nicobar Is (India)
Spilornis kinabaluensis	Kinabalu Serpent-eagle	K*	Malaysia
Spilornis elgini	Dark Serpent-eagle	K*	Andaman Is (India)
Eutriorchis astur	Madagascar Serpent Eagle	E	Madagascar
Accipiter nanus	Small Sparrowhawk	K*	Indonesia
Accipiter brachyurus	New Britain Sparrowhawk	K*	Papua New Guinea
Accipiter imitator	Imitator Sparrowhawk	K*	Papua New Guinea, Solomon Is
Accipiter collaris	Semi-collared Sparrowhawk	K*	Colombia, Ecuador, Peru, Venezuela
Accipiter gundlachii	Gundlach's Hawk	K*	Cuba
Accipiter poliogaster	Grey-bellied Hawk	K*	South America
Leucopternis plumbea	Plumbeous Hawk	K*	Colombia, Ecuador, Panama, Peru
Leucopternis lacernulata	White-necked Hawk	K*	Brazil
Leucopternis occidentalis	Grey-backed Hawk	I	Ecuador
Leucopternis polionota	Mantled Hawk	I	Argentina, Brazil, Paraguay
Harpyhaliaetus solitarius	Solitary Eagle	K*	Colombia, Costa Rica, Ecuador, Guatemala, Honduras, Mexico, Panama, Peru, Venezuela
Harpyhaliaetus coronatus	Crowned Eagle	K*	Argentina, Bolivia, Brazil, Paraguay, Uruguay
Buteo ridgwayi	Ridgway's Hawk	K*	Dominican Republic, Haiti
Buteo galapagoensis	Galapagos Hawk	R	Galapagos (Ecuador)
Buteo solitarius	Hawaiian Hawk	R	Hawaiian Is (U.S.A.)
Buteo ventralis	Red-tailed Hawk	K*	Argentina, Chile
Morphus guianensis	Crested Eagle	R	South and Central America

Harpia harpyja	Harpy Eagle	R	South and Central America
Harpyopsis novaeguineae	New Guinea Harpy Eagle	K*	Indonesia, Papua New Guinea
Pithecophaga jefferyi	Philippine Eagle	E	Philippines
Aquila adalberti	Spanish Imperial Eagle	E	Portugal, Spain
Aquila heliaca	Imperial Eagle	K*	Western Palearctic
Spizaetus bartelsi	Javan Hawk-eagle	K*	Indonesia
Spizaetus philippensis	Philippine Hawk-eagle	K*	Philippines
Family Falconidae			
Micrastur plumbeus	Plumbeous Forest-falcon	K*	Brazil, Colombia, Ecuador
Micrastur buckleyi	Traylor's Forest-falcon	K*	Ecuador, Peru
Falco punctatus	Mauritius Kestrel	E	Mauritius
Falco deiroleucus	Orange-breasted Falcon	K*	South and Central America
Order GALLIFORMES			
Family Megapodiidae			
Megapodius nicobariensis	Nicobar Scrubfowl		India
Megapodius bernsteinii	Sula Scrubfowl	K*	Indonesia
Megapodius laperouse	Micronesian Scrubfowl	R	Belau, Northern Mariana Is (U.S.A.)
Megapodius pritchardii	Niuafo'ou Scrubfowl	K*	Tonga
Megapodius wallacei	Moluccan Scrubfowl	K*	Indonesia
Leipoa ocellata	Malleefowl	K*	Australia
Aepypodius bruijnii	Waigeo Brush-turkey	K*	Indonesia
Macrocephalon maleo	Maleo	V	Indonesia
Family Cracidae			
Ortalis erythroptera	Rufous-headed Chachalaca	K*	Ecuador, Peru
Penelope barbata	Bearded Guan	K*	Ecuador, Peru
Penelope dabbenei	Red-faced Guan	K*	Argentina, Bolivia
Penelope albipennis	White-winged Guan	E	Peru
Penelope perspicax	Cauca Guan	E	Colombia
Penelope jacucaca	White-browed Guan	K*	Brazil
Penelope ochrogaster	Chestnut-bellied Guan	K*	Brazil
Pipile jacutinga	Black-fronted Piping Guan	E	Argentina, Brazil, Paraguay
Penelopina nigra	Highland Guan	K*	El Salvador, Guatemala, Honduras, Mexico, Nicaragua
Oreophasis derbianus	Horned Guan	E	Guatemala, Mexico
Mitu mitu	Alagoas Curassow	E	Brazil
Pauxi pauxi	Northern Helmeted Curassow	K*	Colombia, Venezuela
Pauxi unicornis	Southern Helmeted Curassow	K*	Bolivia, Peru

Crax alberti	Blue-billed Curassow	V	Colombia
Crax globulosa	Wattled Curassow	K*	Bolivia, Brazil, Colombia, Ecuador, Peru
Crax blumenbachii	Red-billed Curassow	E	Brazil
Family Meleagridae			
Agriocharis ocellata	Ocellated Turkey	K*	Mexico, Guatemala, Belize
Family Phasianidae			
Dendrortyx barbatus	Bearded Wood Partridge	K*	Mexico
Odontophorus hyperythrus	Chestnut Wood Quail	K*	Colombia
Odontophorus strophium	Gorgeted Wood Quail	E	Colombia
Tetraogallus altaicus	Altai Snowcock	K*	Mongolia, U.S.S.R.
Francolinus ochropectus	Djibouti Francolin	E	Djibouti
Francolinus camerunensis	Mount Cameroon Francolin	R	Cameroon
Francolinus swierstrai	Swierstra's Francolin	I	Angola
Francolinus nahani	Nahan's Francolin	R	Uganda, Zaire
Francolinus gularis	Swamp Partridge	K*	Bangladesh, India, Nepal
Perdicula manipurensis	Manipur Bush Quail	K*	Bangladesh, India
Arborophila atrogularis	White-cheeked Partridge	K*	India, Burma
Arborophila rufipectus	Sichuan Partridge	K*	China
Arborophila gingica	Rickett's Partridge	K*	China
Arborophila davidi	Orange-necked Partridge	K*	Viet Nam
Arborophila cambodiana	Chestnut-headed Partridge	K*	Kampuchea, Thailand
Arborophila ardens	White-eared Partridge	K*	China
Arborophila charltonii	Chestnut-necklaced Partridge	K*	Indonesia, Malaysia, Thailand
Ophrysia superciliosa	Himalayan Quail	K*	India
Tragopan melanocephalus	Western Tragopan	E	India, Pakistan
Tragopan blythi	Blyth's Tragopan	R	Bhutan, Burma, China, India
Tragopan caboti	Cabot's Tragopan	E	China
Lophophorus sclateri	Sclater's Monal	R	Burma, China, India
Lophophorus lhuysii	Chinese Monal	E	China
Lophura imperialis	Imperial Pheasant	V	Laos, Viet Nam
Lophura edwardsi	Edwards's Pheasant	V	Viet Nam
Lophura hatinhensis	Viet Nam Pheasant	K*	Viet Nam
Lophura swinhoii	Swinhoe's Pheasant	V	Taiwan
Lophura ignita	Crested Fireback	K*	Burma, Indonesia, Malaysia, Thailand
Lophura diardi	Siamese Fireback	K*	Kampuchea, Laos, Thailand, Viet Nam
Lophura bulweri	Bulwer's Pheasant	V	Indonesia, Malaysia

Crossoptilon crossoptilon	White Eared-pheasant	V	Burma, China, India
Crossoptilon mantchuricum	Brown Eared-pheasant	E	China
Crossoptilon auritum	Blue Eared-pheasant	K*	China
Catreus wallichi	Cheer Pheasant	E	India, Nepal, Pakistan
Syrmaticus ellioti	Elliot's Pheasant	E	China
Syrmaticus humiae	Hume's Pheasant	R	Burma, China, India
Syrmaticus mikado	Mikado Pheasant	V	Taiwan
Syrmaticus reevesi	Reeves's Pheasant	K*	China
Chrysolophus amherstiae	Lady Amherst's Pheasant	K*	China
Polyplectron germaini	Germain's Peacock-pheasant	K*	Viet Nam
Polyplectron malacense	Malaysian Peacock-pheasant	K*	Burma, Malaysia, Thailand
Polyplectron schleiermacheri	Bornean Peacock-pheasant	K*	Indonesia
Polyplectron emphanum	Palawan Peacock-pheasant	V	Philippines
Rheinardia ocellata	Crested Argus	R	Laos, Malaysia, Viet Nam
Pavo muticus	Green Peafowl	V	Burma, China, Indonesia, Kampuchea, Laos, Thailand, Viet Nam
Afropavo congensis	Congo Peacock	S	Zaire
Family Numididae			
Agelastes meleagrides	White-breasted Guineafowl	E	West Africa
Family Tetraonidae			
Tetrao mlokosiewiczi	Caucasian Black Grouse	K*	Iran, Turkey, U.S.S.R.
Order GRUIFORMES			
Family Mesitornithidae			
Mesitornis variegata	White-breasted Mesite	R	Madagascar
Mesitornis unicolor	Brown Mesite	K	Madagascar
Monias benschi	Subdesert Mesite	R	Madagascar
Family Turnicidae			
Turnix everetti	Sumba Buttonquail	K*	Indonesia
Turnix worcesteri	Worcester's Buttonquail	K*	Philippines
Turnix melanogaster	Black-breasted Buttonquail	K*	Australia
Family Pedionomidae			
Pedionomus torquatus	Plains-wanderer	K*	Australia

Family Gruidae			
Grus nigricollis	Black-necked Crane	V	Bhutan, Burma, China, India, Viet Nam
Grus monacha	Hooded Crane	V	China, Japan, North Korea, South Korea, U.S.S.R.
Grus japonensis	Japanese Crane	V	China, Japan, North Korea, South Korea, U.S.S.R.
Grus americana	Whooping Crane	E	Canada, U.S.A.
Grus vipio	White-naped Crane	V	China, Japan, North Korea, South Korea, U.S.S.R.
Grus leucogeranus	Siberian Crane	V	Afghanistan, China, India, Iran, U.S.S.R.
Bugeranus carunculatus	Wattled Crane	S	Ethiopia, Central and southern Africa
Family Rallidae			
Rallus okinawae	Okinawa Rail	K*	Japan
Rallus wetmorei	Plain-flanked Rail	K*	Venezuela
Rallus antarcticus	Austral Rail	K*	Argentina, Chile
Rallus semiplumbeus	Bogota Rail	V	Colombia
Rallus muelleri	Auckland Island Rail	I	New Zealand
Rallus owstoni	Guam Rail	V	Guam (U.S.A.)
Atlantisia rogersi	Inaccessible Rail	R	Inaccessible I. (U.K.)
Tricholimnas lafresnayanus	New Caledonian Rail	K*	New Caledonia (France)
Tricholimnas sylvestris	Lord Howe Island Woodhen	E	Lord Howe I. (Australia)
Aramidopsis plateni	Snoring Rail	K*	Indonesia
Cyanolimnas cerverai	Zapata Rail	R	Cuba
Nesoclopeus woodfordi	Woodford's Rail	K*	Papua New Guinea, Solomon Is
Nesoclopeus peociloptera	Barred-wing Rail	E	Fiji
Gymnocrex rosenbergii	Bald-faced Rail	K*	Indonesia
Habroptila wallacii	Invisible Rail	K*	Indonesia
Crex crex	Corncrake	K*	Africa, Western Palearctic
Porzana spiloptera	Dot-winged Crake	K*	Argentina, Uruguay
Nesophylax ater	Henderson Island Rail	K*	Henderson I. (U.K.)
Laterallus xenopterus	Horqueta or Rufous-faced Crake	K*	Brazil, Paraguay
Laterallus levraudi	Rusty-flanked Crake	K*	Venezuela
Coturnicops exquisita	Siberian Crake	K*	China, Japan, South Korea, U.S.S.R.
Sarothrura ayresi	White-winged Flufftail	I	Ethiopia, southern Africa
Sarothrura watersi	Slender-billed Flufftail	I	Madagascar
Amaurornis olivieri	Sakalava Rail	K	Madagascar

Gallinula comeri	Gough Moorhen	R	Gough I. (U.K.)
Gallinula sylvestris	San Cristobal Mountain Rail	I	Solomon Is
Notornis mantelli	Takahe	E	New Zealand
Fulica cornuta	Horned Coot	R	Argentina, Bolivia, Chile
Family Heliornithidae			
Heliopais personata	Masked Finfoot	K*	Bangladesh, Burma, India, Indonesia, Malaysia, Thailand
Family Rhynochetidae			
Rhynochetos jubatus	Kagu	E	New Caledonia (France)
Family Otididae			
Tetrax tetrax	Little Bustard	R	Western Palearctic
Otis tarda	Great Bustard	R	Palearctic
Ardeotis nigriceps	Great Indian Bustard	V	India
Chlamydotis undulata	Houbara Bustard	K*	Western Palearctic
Houbaropsis bengalensis	Bengal Florican	E	India, Kampuchea, Nepal
Sypheotides indica	Lesser Florican	E	India
Order CHARADRIIFORMES			
Family Haematopodidae			
Haematopus meadewaldoi	Canarian Black Oystercatcher	Ex	Canary Is (Spain)
Haematopus chathamensis	Chatham Island Oystercatcher	E	Chatham Is (New Zealand)
Family Recurvirostridae			
Himantopus novaezeelandia	Black Stilt	E	New Zealand
Family Charadriidae			
Chettusia gregaria	Sociable Plover	K*	Asia, north-east Africa
Vanellus macropterus	Javan Wattled Lapwing	I	Indonesia
Charadrius melodus	Piping Plover	K*	Canada, U.S.A.
Charadrius thoracicus	Madagascar Plover	R	Madagascar
Charadrius sanctaehelenae	St. Helena Plover	R	St. Helena (U.K.)
Charadrius rubricollis	Hooded Plover	K*	Australia
Thinornis novaeseelandia	New Zealand Shore Plover	E	New Zealand
Family Scolopacidae			
Numenius borealis	Eskimo Curlew	E	Canada, U.S.A.
Numenius tahitiensis	Bristle-thighed Curlew	K*	Alaska (U.S.A.), Pacific Ocean

Numenius tenuirostris	Slender-billed Curlew	K*	Western Palearctic
Tringa guttifer	Spotted Greenshank	I	Bangladesh, Burma, China, Hong Kong, Japan, U.S.S.R.
Prosobonia cancellatus	Tuamotu Sandpiper	V	Tuamotu Archipelago (France)
Scolopax celebensis	Sulawesi Woodcock	K*	Indonesia
Scolopax rochussenii	Obi Woodcock	K*	Indonesia
Coenocorypha aucklandica	New Zealand Snipe	R	New Zealand
Gallinago nemoricola	Wood Snipe	K*	Bhutan, India, Nepal, Pakistan
Limnodromus semipalmatus	Asian Dowitcher	R	Asia
Calidris paramelanotos	Cox's Sandpiper	K*	Australia
Eurynorhynchus pygmeus	Spoon-billed Sandpiper	K*	U.S.S.R., South-east Asia
Family Glareolidae			
Cursorius bitorquatus	Jerdon's Courser	K*	India
Family Laridae			
Larus pacificus	Pacific Gull	K*	Australia
Larus atlanticus	Olrog's Gull	K*	Argentina
Larus fuliginosus	Lava Gull	K*	Galapagos (Ecuador)
Larus leucophthalmus	White-eyed Gull	K*	Red Sea
Larus audouinii	Audouin's Gull	R	Mediterranean, Morocco
Larus relictus	Relict Gull	R	China, Mongolia, U.S.S.R., Viet Nam
Larus saundersi	Saunder's Gull	K*	China, Hong Kong, Japan, Mongolia, South Korea, Taiwan
Sterna virgata	Kerguelen Tern	K*	Prince Edward I. (South Africa), Crozet and Kerguelen Is (France)
Sterna albostriata	Black-fronted Tern	K*	New Zealand
Sterna balaenarum	Damara Tern	R	South Africa, Namibia
Sterna bernsteini	Chinese Crested Tern	I	China, Indonesia, Malaysia, Thailand
Family Alcidae			
Synthliboramphus wumizusume	Japanese Murrelet	K*	Japan, North Korea, South Korea, U.S.S.R.
Order COLUMBIFORMES			
Family Columbidae			
Columba eversmanni	Pale-backed Pigeon	K*	Afghanistan, India, Iran, Pakistan, U.S.S.R.

Columba oliviae	Somali Pigeon	R	Somalia
Columba trocaz	Madeira Laurel-pigeon	R	Madeira (Portugal)
Columba bollii	Dark-tailed Laurel-pigeon	R	Canary Is (Spain)
Columba junoniae	White-tailed Laurel-pigeon	R	Canary Is (Spain)
Columba thomensis	Maroon Wood-pigeon	K*	Sao Tomé
Columba elphinstonii	Nilgiri Wood-pigeon	K*	India
Columba torringtoni	Sri Lanka Wood-pigeon	K*	Sri Lanka
Columba punicea	Pale-capped Wood-pigeon	K*	Bhutan, Burma, China, India, Thailand
Columba argentina	Grey Wood-pigeon	K*	Indonesia, Malaysia
Columba pallidiceps	Yellow-legged Wood-pigeon	K*	Papua New Guinea, Solomon Is
Columba caribaea	Ring-tailed Wood-pigeon	K*	Jamaica
Nesoenas mayeri	Pink Pigeon	E	Mauritius
Zenaida graysoni	Socorro Dove	K*	Mexico
Columbina cyanopis	Blue-eyed Ground Dove	K*	Brazil
Claravis godefrida	Purple-winged Ground Dove	V	Argentina, Brazil, Paraguay
Leptotila wellsi	Grenada Dove	I	Grenada
Leptotila ochraceiventris	Ochre-bellied Dove	K*	Ecuador, Peru
Leptotila conoveri	Tolima Dove	I	Colombia
Geotrygon caniceps	Grey-headed Quail Dove	K*	Cuba, Dominican Republic
Starnoenas cyanocephala	Blue-headed Quail Dove	K*	Cuba
Gallicolumba platenae	Mindoro Bleeding-heart	K*	Philippines
Gallicolumba keayi	Negros Bleeding-heart	K*	Philippines
Gallicolumba menagei	Sulu Bleeding-heart	K*	Philippines
Gallicolumba erythroptera	Society Islands Ground-dove	I	Society Is, Tuamotu Archipelago (France)
Gallicolumba sanctaecrucis	Santa Cruz Ground-dove	K*	Solomon Is, Vanuatu
Gallicolumba salamonis	Thick-billed Ground-dove	K*	Solomon Is
Gallicolumba rubescens	Marquesas Ground-dove	I	Marquesas (France)
Gallicolumba hoedtii	Wetar Ground-dove	K*	Indonesia
Microgoura meeki	Solomon Island Crowned Pigeon	Ex	Solomon Is
Goura scheepmakeri	Scheepmaker's Crowned Pigeon	K*	Indonesia, Papua New Guinea
Goura victoria	Victoria Crowned Pigeon	K*	Indonesia, Papua New Guinea
Didunculus strigirostris	Tooth-billed Pigeon	V	Western Samoa
Treron teysmanni	Sumba Green-pigeon	K*	Indonesia
Treron floris	Flores Green-pigeon	K*	Indonesia
Treron psittacea	Timor Green-pigeon	K*	Indonesia
Treron capellei	Large Green-pigeon	K*	Burma, Indonesia, Malaysia, Thailand
Ptilinopus dohertyi	Red-naped Fruit-dove	K*	Indonesia

Ptilinopus marchei	Flame-breasted Fruit-dove	K*	Philippines
Ptilinopus roseicapilla	Marianas Fruit-dove	V	Guam, Northern Mariana Is (U.S.A.)
Ptilinopus huttoni	Rapa Fruit-dove	R	Austral Is (France)
Ptilinopus mercierii	Marquesas Fruit-dove	K*	Marquesas Is (France)
Ptilinopus arcanus	Negros Fruit-dove	K*	Philippines
Drepanoptila holosericea	Cloven-feathered Dove	V	New Caledonia (France)
Ducula mindorensis	Mindoro Imperial-pigeon	K*	Philippines
Ducula carola	Spotted Imperial-pigeon	K*	Philippines
Ducula aurorae	Society Islands Imperial-pigeon	V	Society Is, Tuamotu Archipelago (France)
Ducula galeata	Marquesas Imperial-pigeon	E	Marquesas Is (France)
Ducula pistrinaria	Island Imperial-pigeon	K*	Papua New Guinea, Solomon Is
Ducula whartoni	Christmas Imperial-pigeon	V	Christmas I. (Australia)
Ducula goliath	Giant Imperial-pigeon	V	New Caledonia (France)
Order PSITTACIFORMES			
Family Psittacidae			
Eos cyanogenia	Biak Red Lory	K*	Indonesia
Eos histrio	Red-and-blue Lory	K*	Indonesia
Lorius domicella	Purple-naped Lory	K*	Indonesia
Vini peruviana	Tahiti Lorikeet	R	Society Is, Tuamotu Archipelago (France), Cook Is
Vini ultramarina	Ultramarine Lorikeet	R	Marquesas Is (France)
Charmosyna toxopei	Blue-fronted Lorikeet	K*	Indonesia
Charmosyna multistriata	Streaked Lorikeet	K*	Indonesia
Charmosyna diadema	New Caledonian Lorikeet	K*	New Caledonia (France)
Cacatua sulphurea	Yellow-crested Cockatoo	K*	Indonesia
Cacatua moluccensis	Salmon-crested Cockatoo	K*	Indonesia
Cacatua alba	White Cockatoo	K*	Indonesia
Cacatua haematuropygia	Red-vented Cockatoo	K*	Philippines
Cacatua goffini	Tanimbar Corella	K*	Indonesia
Prioniturus luconensis	Green-crowned Racket-tailed Parrot	K*	Philippines
Prioniturus discurus	Blue-headed Racket-tailed Parrot	K*	Philippines
Prioniturus montanus	Red-crowned Racket-tailed Parrot	K*	Philippines
Psittrichas fulgidus	Vulturine Parrot	K*	Indonesia, Papua New Guinea
Psephotus dissimilis	Hooded Parrot	K*	Australia
Psephotus chrysopterygius	Golden-shouldered Parrot	R	Australia
Psephotus pulcherrimus	Paradise Parrot	E	Australia
Cyanoramphus unicolor	Antipodes Island Parrot	K*	New Zealand

Cyanoramphus malherbi	Orange-fronted Parakeet	E	New Zealand
Neophema chrysogaster	Orange-bellied Parrot	R	Australia
Neophema splendida	Scarlet-chested Parakeet	R	Australia
Pezoporus wallicus	Ground Parrot	E	Australia
Geopsittacus occidentalis	Night Parrot	I	Australia
Agapornis nigrigenis	Black-cheeked Lovebird	R	Zambia
Loriculus flosculus	Wallace's Hanging Parrot	K*	Indonesia
Loriculus catamene	Sangihe Hanging Parrot	K*	Indonesia
Psittacula intermedia	Rothschild's Parakeet	K*	India
Psittacula caniceps	Nicobar Parakeet	K*	Nicobar Is (India)
Psittacula eques	Mauritius Parakeet	E	Mauritius
Anodorhynchus hyacinthinus	Hyacinth Macaw	K*	Bolivia, Brazil, Paraguay
Anodorhynchus glaucus	Glaucous Macaw	Ex	Argentina, Brazil, Paraguay, Uruguay
Anodorhynchus leari	Indigo Macaw	E	Brazil
Cyanopsitta spixii	Little Blue Macaw	E	Brazil
Ara glaucogularis (= *A. caninde*)	Blue-throated Macaw	I	Bolivia
Ara rubrogenys	Red-fronted Macaw	K*	Bolivia
Ara maracana	Blue-winged Macaw	K*	Argentina, Brazil, Paraguay
Aratinga guarouba	Golden Conure	V	Brazil
Aratinga euops	Cuban Conure	K*	Cuba
Aratinga auricapilla	Golden-capped Conure	K*	Brazil
Leptosittaca branickii	Golden-plumed Conure	K*	Colombia, Ecuador, Peru
Ognorhynchus icterotis	Yellow-eared Conure	V	Colombia, Ecuador
Rhynchopsitta pachyrhyncha	Thick-billed Parrot	V	Mexico
Rhynchopsitta terrisi	Maroon-fronted Parrot	E	Mexico
Pyrrhura cruentata	Blue-throated Conure	R	Brazil
Pyrrhura perlata	Pearly Conure	K*	Brazil
Pyrrhura hypoxantha	Yellow-sided Conure	K*	Brazil
Pyrrhura albipectus	White-necked Conure	K*	Ecuador
Pyrrhura calliptera	Brown-breasted Conure	K*	Colombia
Enicognathus leptorhynchus	Slender-billed Conure	K*	Chile
Bolborhynchus ferrugineifrons	Rufous-fronted Parakeet	I	Colombia
Brotogeris pyrrhopterus	Grey-cheeked Parakeet	K*	Ecuador, Peru
Touit melanonota	Brown-backed Parrotlet	R	Brazil
Touit surda	Golden-tailed Parrotlet	I	Brazil
Touit stictoptera	Spot-winged Parrotlet	K*	Colombia, Ecuador
Pionopsitta pileata	Pileated Parrot	K*	Argentina, Brazil, Paraguay
Hapalopsittaca amazonina	Rusty-faced Parrot	K*	Colombia, Ecuador, Venezuela
Amazona vittata	Puerto Rican Amazon	E	Puerto Rico

Amazona pretrei	Red-spectacled Amazon	V	Argentina, Brazil, Paraguay, Uruguay
Amazona viridigenalis	Red-crowned or Green-cheeked Amazon	K*	Mexico
Amazona brasiliensis	Red-tailed Amazon	E	Brazil
Amazona rhodocorytha	Red-browed Amazon	K*	Brazil
Amazona xanthops	Yellow-faced Amazon	K*	Brazil
Amazona barbadensis	Yellow-shouldered Amazon	K*	Netherlands Antilles, Venezuela
Amazona vinacea	Vinaceous Amazon	K*	Argentina, Brazil, Paraguay
Amazona versicolor	St. Lucia Amazon	E	St. Lucia
Amazona arausiaca	Red-necked Amazon	E	Dominica
Amazona guildingii	St. Vincent Amazon	E	St. Vincent
Amazona imperialis	Imperial Amazon	E	Dominica
Triclaria malachitacea	Purple-bellied Parrot	K*	Brazil
Strigops habroptilus	Kakapo	E	New Zealand
Order CUCULIFORMES			
Family Musophagidae			
Tauraco bannermani	Bannerman's Turaco	E	Cameroon
Tauraco ruspolii	Prince Ruspoli's Turaco	R	Ethiopia
Family Cuculidae			
Chrysococcyx rufomerus	Green-cheecked Bronze Cuckoo	K*	Indonesia
Coccyzus ferrugineus	Cocos Cuckoo	K*	Costa Rica
Phaenicophaeus pyrrhocephalus	Red-faced Malkoha	K*	India, Sri Lanka
Neomorphus radiolosus	Banded Ground Cuckoo	K*	Colombia, Ecuador
Carpococcyx radiceus	Sunda Ground Cuckoo	K*	Indonesia, Malaysia
Coua delalandei	Snail-eating Coua	Ex	Madagascar
Centropus chlororhynchus	Green-billed Coucal	K*	Sri Lanka
Centropus steerii	Steere's Coucal	K*	Philippines
Centropus nigrorufus	Javan Coucal	K*	Indonesia
Order STRIGIFORMES			
Family Tytonidae			
Tyto soumagnei	Madagascar Red Owl	I	Madagascar
Tyto nigrobrunnea	Taliabu Owl	K*	Indonesia
Tyto inexspectata	Minahassa Owl	K*	Indonesia
Tyto sororcula	Lesser Masked Owl	K*	Indonesia
Tyto aurantia	Golden Owl	K*	Papua New Guinea
Phodilus prigoginei	Itombwe Owl	I	Burundi, Zaire

Family Strigidae			
Otus sagittatus	White-fronted Scops-owl	K*	Burma, Indonesia, Malaysia, Thailand
Otus ireneae	Sokoke Scops-owl	E	Kenya
Otus stresemanni	Sumatran Scops-owl	K*	Indonesia
Otus angelinae	Javan Scops-owl	K*	Indonesia
Otus alfredi	Flores Scops-owl	K*	Indonesia
Otus mindorensis	Mindoro Scops-owl	K*	Philippines
Otus pauliani	Grand Comoro Scops-owl	R	Comoro Is
Otus insularis	Seychelles Scops-owl	R	Seychelles
Otus hartlaubi	Sao Tomé Scops-owl	R	Sao Tomé
Bubo vosseleri	Usambara Eagle-owl	R	Tanzania
Bubo philippensis	Philippine Eagle-owl	K*	Philippines
Ketupa blakistoni	Blakiston's Fish-owl	K*	China, Japan, U.S.S.R.
Scotopelia ussheri	Rufous Fishing Owl	R	West Africa
Glaucidium albertinum	Albertine Owlet	R	Rwanda, Zaire
Sceloglaux albifacies	Laughing Owl	Ex	New Zealand
Athene blewitti	Forest Owlet	I	India
Strix davidi	David's Owl	K*	China
Order CAPRIMULGIFORMES			
Family Podargidae			
Batrachostomus harterti	Dulit Frogmouth	K*	Indonesia, Malaysia
Family Nyctibiidae			
Nyctibius aethereus	Long-tailed Potoo	K*	Brazil, Colombia, Ecuador, Guyana, Paraguay, Peru, Venezuela
Nyctibius leucopterus	White-winged Potoo	K*	Brazil
Nyctibius bracteatus	Rufous Potoo	K*	Colombia, Ecuador, Guyana, Peru
Family Caprimulgidae			
Eurostopodus diabolicus	Satanic Nightjar	K*	Indonesia
Siphonorhis americanus	Jamaican Least Pauraque	Ex	Jamaica
Caprimulgus noctitherus	Puerto Rican Nightjar	R	Puerto Rico
Caprimulgus candicans	White-winged Nightjar	K*	Brazil, Paraguay
Caprimulgus whitelyi	Roraiman Nightjar	K*	Venezuela
Caprimulgus hirundinaceus	Pygmy Nightjar	K*	Brazil
Caprimulgus ruficollis	Red-necked Nightjar	K*	Spain, Portugal, West Africa
Caprimulgus centralasicus	Vaurie's Nightjar	K*	China
Caprimulgus pulchellus	Salvadori's Nightjar	K*	Indonesia

Macropsalis creagra	Long-trained Nightjar	K*	Argentina, Brazil
Eleothreptus anomalus	Sickle-winged Nightjar	K*	Argentina, Brazil, Paraguay, Uruguay
Order APODIFORMES			
Family Apodidae			
Cypseloides lemosi	White-chested Swift	K*	Colombia
Hydrochous gigas	Giant Swiftlet	K*	Indonesia, Malaysia
Collocalia elaphra	Seychelles Swiftlet	R	Seychelles
Aerodramus leucophaeus	Tahiti Swiftlet	K*	Society Is (France)
Aerodramus sawtelli	Atiu Swiftlet	K*	Cook Is
Schoutedenapus schoutedeni	Schouteden's Swift	I	Zaire
Apus sladeniae	Fernando Po Swift	K	Angola, Cameroon, Fernando Po (Equatorial Guinea), Nigeria
Apus acuticauda	Dark-rumped Swift	K*	India
Family Trochilidae			
Glaucis dohrnii	Hook-billed Hermit	E	Brazil
Threnetes niger	Sooty Barbthroat	K*	French Guiana
Phaethornis idaliae	Minute Hermit	K*	Brazil
Campylopterus ensipennis	White-tailed Sabrewing	K*	Tobago (Trinidad), Venezuela
Campylopterus villaviscensio	Napo Sabrewing	K*	Ecuador
Avocettula recurvirostris	Fiery-tailed Awlbill	K*	Brazil, French Guiana, Guyana, Venezuela
Popelairia letitiae	Coppery Thorntail	K*	Bolivia
Lepidopyga lilliae	Sapphire-bellied Hummingbird	K*	Colombia
Amazilia luciae	Honduran Emerald	K*	Honduras
Amazilia distans	Tachira Emerald	K*	Venezuela
Amazilia boucardi	Mangrove Hummingbird	K*	Costa Rica
Amazilia castaneiventris	Chestnut-bellied Hummingbird	K*	Colombia
Eupherusa poliocerca	White-tailed Hummingbird	K*	Mexico
Eupherusa cyanophrys	Oaxaca or Blue-capped Hummingbird	K*	Mexico
Anthocephala floriceps	Blossomcrown	K*	Colombia
Phlogophilus hemileucurus	Ecuadorean Piedtail	K*	Ecuador
Phlogophilus harterti	Peruvian Piedtail	K*	Peru
Heliodoxa gularis	Pink-throated Brillant	K*	Ecuador, Peru
Hylonympha macrocerca	Scissor-tailed Hummingbird	K*	Venezuela
Aglaeactis aliciae	Purple-backed Sunbeam	K*	Peru
Coeligena prunellei	Black Inca	I	Colombia

Sephanoides fernandensis	Juan Fernandez Firecrown	K*	Juan Fernandez Is (Chile)
Heliangelus viola	Purple-throated Sunangel	K*	Ecuador, Peru
Heliangelus regalis	Royal Sunangel	K*	Peru
Eriocnemis nigrivestris	Black-breasted Puffleg	K*	Ecuador
Eriocnemis godini	Turquoise-throated Puffleg	K*	Ecuador
Eriocnemis mirabilis	Colourful Puffleg	K*	Colombia
Eriocnemis derbyi	Black-thighed Puffleg	K*	Colombia, Ecuador
Haplophaedia lugens	Hoary Puffleg	K*	Colombia, Ecuador
Metallura odomae	Neblina Metaltail	K*	Peru
Metallura baroni	Violet-throated Metaltail	K*	Ecuador
Taphrolesbia griseventris	Grey-bellied Comet	K*	Peru
Augastes scutatus	Hyacinth Visorbearer	K*	Brazil
Augastes lumachellus	Hooded Visorbearer	K*	Brazil
Loddigesia mirabilis	Marvellous Spatuletail	K*	Peru
Calypte helenae	Bee Hummingbird	K*	Cuba
Eulidia yarrellii	Chilean Woodstar	R	Chile
Acestrura bombus	Little Woodstar	K*	Ecuador, Peru
Acestrura berlepschi	Esmeraldas Woodstar	K*	Ecuador
Selasphorus ardens	Glow-throated Hummingbird	K*	Panama
Order TROGONIFORMES			
Family Trogonidae			
Pharomachrus mocinno	Resplendent Quetzal	V	Central America
Euptilotis neoxenus	Eared Trogon	K*	Mexico, U.S.A.
Trogon bairdii	Baird's Trogon	K*	Costa Rica, Panama
Order CORACIIFORMES			
Family Alcedinidae			
Alcedo hercules	Blyth's Kingfisher	K*	Bhutan, Burma, China, India, Nepal, Viet Nam
Ceyx melanurus	Jungle Kingfisher	K*	Philippines
Halcyon winchelli	Winchell's Kingfisher	K*	Philippines
Halcyon lazuli	Lazuli Kingfisher	K*	Indonesia
Halcyon albonotata	New Britain Kingfisher	K*	Papua New Guinea
Halcyon australasia	Cinnamon-banded Kingfisher	K*	Indonesia
Halcyon ruficollaris	Mangaia Kingfisher	K*	Cook Is
Halcyon gambieri	Tuamotu Kingfisher	K*	Tuamotu Archipelago (France)
Halcyon godeffroyi	Marquesas Kingfisher	K*	Marquesas Is (France)
Halcyon bougainvillei	Moustached Kingfisher	K*	Papua New Guinea, Solomon Is

Halcyon hombroni	Blue-capped Wood Kingfisher	K*	Philippines
Tanysiptera riedelii	Biak Paradise Kingfisher	K*	Indonesia
Family Momotidae			
Electron carinatum	Keel-billed Motmot	K*	Central America
Family Coraciidae			
Brachypteracias leptosomus	Short-legged Ground Roller	R	Madagascar
Brachypteracias squamiger	Scaly Ground Roller	R	Madagascar
Atelornis crossleyi	Rufous-headed Ground Roller	R	Madagascar
Uratelornis chimaera	Long-tailed Ground Roller	R	Madagascar
Family Bucerotidae			
Ptilolaemus tickelli	Brown Hornbill	K*	Burma, India, Laos, Thailand, Viet Nam
Aceros nipalensis	Rufous-necked Hornbill	K*	Bhutan, Burma, India, Kampuchea, Laos, Nepal, Thailand, Viet Nam
Aceros subruficollis	Plain-pouched Hornbill	K*	Burma, Indonesia, Malaysia, Thailand
Aceros narcondami	Narcondam Hornbill	K*	Andaman Is (India)
Rhyticeros everetti	Sumba Hornbill	K*	Indonesia
Anthracoceros montani	Sulu Hornbill	K*	Philippines
Rhinoplax vigil	Helmeted Hornbill	I	Burma, Indonesia, Malaysia, Thailand
Family Galbulidae			
Jacamaralcyon tridactyla	Three-toed Jacamar	K*	Brazil
Family Capitonidae			
Capito hypoleucus	White-mantled Barbet	K*	Colombia
Semnornis ramphastinus	Toucan Barbet	V	Colombia, Ecuador
Megalaima javensis	Black-banded Barbet	K*	Indonesia
Pogoniulus makawai	White-chested Tinkerbird	I	Zambia
Family Indicatoridae			
Melignomon eisentrauti	Yellow-footed Honeyguide	K	Cameroon, Ghana, Liberia
Family Ramphastidae			
Aulacorhynchus huallagae	Yellow-browed Toucanet	K*	Peru

Family Picidae			
Picumnus steindachneri	Speckle-chested Piculet	K*	Peru
Picoides borealis	Red-cockaded Woodpecker	V	U.S.A.
Dryocopus galeatus	Helmeted Woodpecker	E	Argentina, Brazil, Paraguay
Dryocopus schulzi	Black-bodied Woodpecker	K*	Argentina, Paraguay
Campephilus robustus	Robust Woodpecker	K*	Argentina, Brazil, Paraguay
Campephilus principalis	Ivory-billed Woodpecker	E	Cuba, U.S.A.
Campephilus imperialis	Imperial Woodpecker	E	Mexico
Picus rabieri	Red-collared Woodpecker	K*	Laos, Viet Nam
Sapheopipo noguchii	Okinawa Woodpecker	E	Japan
Order PASSERIFORMES			
Family Eurylaimidae			
Pseudocalyptomena graueri	African Green Broadbill	R	Uganda, Zaire
Eurylaimus steeri	Wattled Broadbill	K*	Philippines
Family Dendrocolaptidae			
Xiphocolaptes franciscanus	Snethlage's Woodcreeper	K*	Brazil
Family Furnariidae			
Cinclodes palliatus	White-bellied Cinclodes	K*	Peru
Cinclodes aricomae	Stout-billed Cinclodes	K*	Peru
Aphrastura masafuerae	Masafuera Rayadito	K*	Chile
Leptasthenura xenothorax	White-browed Tit Spinetail	K*	Peru
Synallaxis infuscata	Plain Spinetail	K*	Brazil
Synallaxis courseni	Apurimac Spinetail	K*	Peru
Synallaxis cherriei	Chestnut-throated Spinetail	K*	Brazil, Ecuador, Peru
Synallaxis zimmeri	Russet-bellied Spinetail	K*	Peru
Asthenes anthoides	Austral Canastero	K*	Argentina, Chile
Asthenes urubambensis	Line-fronted Canastero	K*	Peru
Thripophaga cherriei	Orinoco Softtail	K*	Venezuela
Thripophaga macroura	Striated Softtail	K*	Brazil
Phacellodomus dorsalis	Chestnut-backed Thornbird	K*	Peru
Phacellodomus dendrocolaptoides	Canebrake Groundcreeper	K*	Argentina, Brazil, Paraguay
Margarornis tatei	White-throated Barbtail	K*	Venezuela
Philydor amaurotis	White-browed Foliage-gleaner	K*	Argentina, Brazil
Philydor novaesi	Alagoas Foliage-gleaner	K*	Brazil
Philydor dimidiatus	Russet-mantled Foliage-gleaner	K*	Brazil, Paraguay
Automolus ruficollis	Rufous-necked Foliage-gleaner	K*	Ecuador, Peru

Automolus rectirostris	Chestnut-capped Foliage-gleaner	K*	Brazil
Automolus erythrocephalus	Henna-hooded Foliage-gleaner	K*	Ecuador, Peru
Megaxenops parnaguae	Great Xenops	K*	Brazil
Family Formicariidae			
Biatas nigropectus	White-bearded Antshrike	K*	Argentina, Brazil
Thamnophilus praecox	Cocha Antshrike	K*	Ecuador, Peru
Clytoctantes alixii	Recurve-billed Bushbird	K*	Colombia, Venezuela
Thamnomanes plumbeus	Plumbeous Antshrike	K*	Brazil
Myrmotherula klagesi	Klages's Antwren	K*	Brazil
Myrmotherula erythronotos	Black-hooded Antwren	E	Brazil
Myrmotherula minor	Salvadori's Antwren	K*	Brazil
Myrmotherula grisea	Ashy Antwren	K*	Bolivia
Herpsilochmus pileatus	Black-capped Antwren	K*	Brazil
Herpsilochmnus parkeri	Ash-throated Antwren	K*	Peru
Formicivora iheringi	Narrow-billed Antwren	V	Brazil
Drymophila genei	Rufous-tailed Antbird	K*	Brazil
Terenura sharpei	Yellow-rumped Antwren	K*	Bolivia, Peru
Terenura sicki	Orange-bellied Antwren	K*	Brazil
Cercomacra brasiliana	Rio de Janeiro Antbird	K*	Brazil
Cercomacra carbonaria	Rio Branco Antbird	K*	Brazil
Pyriglena atra	Fringe-backed Fire-eye	E	Brazil
Rhopornis ardesiaca	Slender Antbird	V	Brazil
Myrmeciza ruficauda	Scalloped Antbird	K*	Brazil
Myrmeciza griseiceps	Grey-headed Antbird	K*	Ecuador, Peru
Myrmeciza stictothorax	Spot-breasted Antbird	K*	Brazil
Rhegmatorhina gymnops	Bare-eyed Antbird	K*	Brazil
Formicarius rufifrons	Rufous-fronted Antthrush	K*	Peru
Grallaria gigantea	Giant Antpitta	K*	Colombia, Ecuador
Grallaria excelsa	Great Antpitta	K*	Venezuela
Grallaria alleni	Moustached Antpitta	I	Colombia
Grallaria chthonia	Tachira Antpitta	K*	Venezuela
Grallaria rufocinerea	Bicolored Antpitta	K*	Colombia
Grallaria milleri	Brown-banded Antpitta	I	Colombia
Grallaricula loricata	Scallop-breasted Antpitta	K*	Venezuela
Grallaricula cucullata	Hooded Antpitta	K*	Colombia, Venezuela
Family Conopophagidae			
Conopophaga roberti	Hooded Gnateater	K*	Brazil

Family Rhinocryptidae			
Merulaxis stresemanni	Stresemann's Bristlefront	I	Brazil
Scytalopus novacapitalis	Brasilia Tapaculo	I	Brazil
Family Cotingidae			
Laniisoma elegans	Shrike-like Cotinga	K*	Bolivia, Brazil, Colombia, Ecuador, Peru, Venezuela
Tijuca condita	Grey-winged Cotinga	K*	Brazil
Carpornis melanocephalus	Black-headed Berryeater	K*	Brazil
Ampelion stresemanni	White-cheeked Cotinga	K*	Peru
Iodopleura pipra	Buff-throated Purpletuft	K*	Brazil
Calyptura cristata	Kinglet Cotinga	I	Brazil
Lipaugus lanioides	Cinnamon-vented Piha	K*	Brazil
Cotinga ridgwayi	Turquoise Cotinga	K*	Costa Rica, Panama
Cotinga maculata	Banded Cotinga	V	Brazil
Xipholena atropurpurea	White-winged Cotinga	V	Brazil
Carpodectes antoniae	Yellow-billed Cotinga	K*	Costa Rica, Panama
Carpodectes hopkei	White Cotinga	K*	Colombia, Ecuador, Panama
Cephalopterus glabricollis	Bare-necked Umbrellabird	K*	Costa Rica, Panama
Cephalopterus penduliger	Long-wattled Umbrellabird	V	Colombia, Ecuador
Family Pipridae			
Piprites pileatus	Black-capped Manakin	K*	Argentina, Brazil
Pipra vilasboasi	Golden-crowned Manakin	K*	Brazil
Family Tyrannidae			
Agriornis albicauda	White-tailed Shrike Tyrant	K*	Argentina, Bolivia, Chile, Ecuador, Peru
Yetapa risoria	Strange-tailed Tyrant	K*	Argentina, Brazil, Paraguay, Uruguay
Xenotriccus calizonus	Belted Flycatcher	K*	Guatemala, Mexico
Ceratotriccus furcatus	Fork-tailed Pygmy Tyrant	K*	Brazil
Idioptilon kaempferi	Kaempfer's Tody Tyrant	K*	Brazil
Pogonotriccus eximius	Southern Bristle Tyrant	K*	Argentina, Brazil, Paraguay
Pogonotriccus venezuelanus	Venezuelan Bristle Tyrant	K*	Venezuela
Anairetes alpinus	Ash-breasted Tit Tyrant	K*	Bolivia, Peru
Culicivora caudacuta	Sharp-tailed Tyrant	K*	Argentina, Bolivia, Brazil, Paraguay
Polystictus pectoralis	Bearded Tachuri	K*	Argentina, Bolivia, Brazil, Colombia, Guyana, Paraguay, Suriname, Venezuela

Polystictus superciliaris	Grey-backed Tachuri	K*	Brazil
Phylloscartes roquettei	Minas Gerais Tyrannulet	K*	Brazil
Phylloscartes paulistus	Sao Paulo Tyrannulet	K*	Brazil, Paraguay
Phylloscartes ceciliae	Long-tailed Tyrannulet	K*	Brazil
Todirostrum viridanum	Short-tailed Tody Flycatcher	K*	Venezuela
Platyrinchus leucoryphus	Russet-winged Spadebill	K*	Brazil, Paraguay
Aphanotriccus capitalis	Tawny-chested Flycatcher	K*	Costa Rica, Nicaragua
Empidonax griseipectus	Grey-breasted Flycatcher	K*	Ecuador, Peru
Alectrurus tricolor	Cock-tailed Tyrant	K*	Argentina, Bolivia, Brazil, Paraguay
Family Phytotomidae			
Phytotoma raimondii	Peruvian Plantcutter	K*	Peru
Family Pittidae			
Pitta schneideri	Schneider's Pitta	K*	Indonesia
Pitta kochi	Whiskered Pitta	K*	Philippines
Pitta ellioti	Bar-bellied Pitta	K*	Kampuchea, Laos, Viet Nam
Pitta gurneyi	Gurney's Pitta	E	Burma, Thailand
Pitta baudi	Blue-headed Pitta	K*	Indonesia
Pitta nympha	Fairy Pitta	K*	China, Japan, Korea, Borneo, Taiwan, Indochina
Pitta superba	Superb Pitta	K*	Manus I. (Papua New Guinea)
Pitta anerythra	Solomon Islands Pitta	K*	Papua New Guinea, Solomon Is
Family Acanthisittidae			
Xenicus longipes	New Zealand Bush Wren	E	New Zealand
Family Philepittidae			
Neodrepanis hypoxantha	Yellow-bellied Sunbird-asity	I	Madagascar
Family Atrichornithidae			
Atrichornis rufescens	Rufous Scrub-bird	R	Australia
Atrichornis clamosus	Noisy Scrub-bird	E	Australia
Family Alaudidae			
Mirafra ashi	Ash's Lark	K	Somalia
Mirafra degodiensis	Degodi Lark	K	Ethiopia
Heteromirafra archeri	Somali Long-clawed Lark	I	Somalia
Heteromirafra sidamoensis	Sidamo Long-clawed Lark	I	Ethiopia

Heteromirafra ruddi	South African Long-clawed Lark	I	Lesotho, South Africa, Swaziland
Spizocorys fringillaris	Botha's Lark	I	South Africa
Alauda razae	Raso Lark	E	Raso (Cape Verde Is)
Family Hirundinidae			
Pseudochelidon sirintarae	White-eyed River Martin	I	Thailand
Callichelidon cyaneoviridis	Bahama Swallow	K*	Bahama Is
Hirundo megaensis	White-tailed Swallow	R	Ethiopia
Hirundo perdita	Red Sea Cliff Swallow	K*	Sudan
Family Motacillidae			
Anthus sokokensis	Sokoke Pipit	V	Kenya, Tanzania
Anthus chloris	Yellow-breasted Pipit	K*	Lesotho, South Africa
Anthus chacoensis	Chaco Pipit	K*	Argentina, Paraguay
Anthus nattereri	Ochre-breasted Pipit	K*	Argentina, Brazil, Paraguay
Family Campephagidae			
Coracina typica	Mauritius Cuckoo-shrike	V	Mauritius
Coracina newtoni	Reunion Cuckoo-shrike	V	Réunion (France)
Coracina coerulescens	Blackish Cuckoo-shrike	K*	Philippines
Coracina ostenta	White-winged Cuckoo-shrike	K*	Philippines
Campephaga lobata	Western Wattled Cuckoo-shrike	V	West Africa
Family Pycnonotidae			
Pycnonotus nieuwenhuisi	Wattled Bulbul	K*	Indonesia
Pycnonotus leucolepis	Spot-winged Bulbul	K*	Liberia
Chlorocichla prigoginei	Prigogine's Greenbul	V	Zaire
Phyllastrephus apperti	Appert's Greenbul	R	Madagascar
Phyllastrephus tenebrosus	Dusky Greenbul	R	Madagascar
Phyllastrephus cinereiceps	Grey-crowned Greenbul	R	Madagascar
Criniger olivaceus	Yellow-throated Olive Greenbul	V	West Africa
Hypsipetes siquijorensis	Mottled-breasted Bulbul	K*	Philippines
Hypsipetes olivaceus	Mauritius Black Bulbul	V	Mauritius
Family Laniidae			
Prionops gabela	Gabela Helmet-shrike	I	Angola
Malaconotus kupeensis	Mount Kupe Bush-shrike	I	Cameroon
Malaconotus gladiator	Green-breasted Bush-shrike	R	Cameroon, Niger
Malaconotus alius	Uluguru Bush-shrike	R	Tanzania

Malaconotus monteiri	Monteiro's Bush-shrike	I	Angola, Cameroon
Lanius newtoni	Sao Tomé Fiscal Shrike	I	Sao Tomé
Family Vangidae			
Xenopirostris damii	Van Dam's Vanga	R	Madagascar
Xenopirostris polleni	Pollen's Vanga	R	Madagascar
Family Cinclidae			
Cinclus schulzi	Rufous-throated Dipper	I	Argentina
Family Troglodytidae			
Hylorchilus sumichrasti	Slender-billed Wren	K*	Mexico
Cistothorus apolinari	Apolinar's Wren	V	Colombia
Ferminia cerverai	Zapata Wren	R	Cuba
Thryothorus nicefori	Niceforo's Wren	K*	Colombia
Troglodytes tanneri	Clarion Wren	K*	Mexico
Family Mimidae			
Mimodes graysoni	Socorro Mockingbird	K*	Mexico
Ramphocinclus brachyurus	White-breasted Thrasher	E	Martinique, St. Lucia
Family Muscicapidae			
Brachypteryx hyperythra	Rusty-bellied Shortwing	K*	China, India
Swynnertonia swynnertoni	Swynnerton's Forest Robin	R	Mozambique, Tanzania, Zimbabwe
Sheppardia gabela	Gabela Akalat	I	Angola
Sheppardia gunningi	East Coast Akalat	R	Kenya, Mozambique, Tanzania
Erithacus ruficeps	Rufous-headed Robin	K*	China, Malaysia
Erithacus obscurus	Black-throated Robin	K*	China, Thailand
Cossypha heinrichi	White-headed Robin-chat	I	Angola, Zaire
Modulatrix orostruthus	Dappled Mountain Robin	R	Mozambique, Tanzania
Dryocichloides montanus	Usambara Ground Robin	R	Tanzania
Dryocichloides lowei	Iringa Ground Robin	R	Tanzania
Alethe choloensis	Thyolo Alethe	E	Malawi, Mozambique
Copsychus sechellarum	Seychelles Magpie-robin	E	Seychelles
Copsychus cebuensis	Black Shama	K*	Philippines
Rhyacornis bicolor	Luzon Redstart	K*	Philippines
Cinclidium frontale	Blue-fronted Robin	K*	China, India, Laos, Nepal, Thailand, Viet Nam
Cochoa beccari	Sumatran Cochoa	K*	Indonesia

Cochoa azurea	Javan Cochoa	K*	Indonesia
Myadestes leucogenys	Rufous-brown Solitaire	K*	Brazil, Ecuador, Guyana, Peru, Venezuela
Myadestes myadestinus	Kamao	K*	Hawaiian Is (U.S.A.)
Myadestes lanaiensis	Olomao	K*	Hawaiian Is (U.S.A.)
Myadestes palmeri	Puaiohi	E	Hawaiian Is (U.S.A.)
Saxicola macrorhyncha	White-browed Bushchat	K*	India, Pakistan
Saxicola insignis	Hodgson's Bushchat	K*	China, India, Mongolia, Nepal
Saxicola dacotiae	Fuerteventura Stonechat	R	Canary Is (Spain)
Monticola bensoni	Benson's Rockthrush	K	Madagascar
Myiophoneus blighi	Sri Lanka Whistling-thrush	K*	Sri Lanka
Geomalia heinrichi	Geomalia	K*	Indonesia
Zoothera schistacea	Slaty-backed Thrush	K*	Indonesia
Zoothera erythronota	Red-backed Thrush	K*	Indonesia
Zoothera peronii	Orange-banded Thrush	K*	Indonesia
Zoothera everetti	Everett's Thrush	K*	Indonesia, Malaysia
Zoothera spiloptera	Spot-winged Thrush	K*	Sri Lanka
Zoothera machiki	Fawn-breasted Thrush	K*	Indonesia
Zoothera amami	Amami Thrush	K*	Japan
Zoothera margaretae	San Cristobal Thrush	K*	Solomon Is
Turdus oberlaenderi	Forest Ground-thrush	R	Madagascar
Turdus kibalensis	Kibale Ground-thrush	I	Uganda
Turdus fischeri	Spotted Ground-thrush	R	East Africa, South Africa, Zaire
Turdus helleri	Taita Thrush	E	Kenya
Turdus menachensis	Yemen Thrush	K*	North Yemen, Saudi Arabia
Turdus feae	Grey-sided Thrush	K*	Burma, China, India, Thailand
Pellorneum palustre	Marsh Babbler	K*	Bangladesh, India
Trichastoma perspicillatum	Black-browed Babbler	K*	Indonesia
Leonardina woodi	Bagobo Babbler	K*	Philippines
Jabouilleia danjoui	Short-tailed Scimitar-babbler	K*	Viet Nam
Ptilocichla leucogrammica	Bornean Wren-babbler	K*	Indonesia, Malaysia
Ptilocichla mindanensis	Striated Wren-babbler	K*	Philippines
Napothera rabori	Rabor's Wren-babbler	K*	Philippines
Spelaeornis badeigularis	Rusty-throated Wren-babbler	K*	India
Stachyris rodolphei	Deignan's Babbler	K*	Thailand
Stachyris striata	Striped Babbler	K*	Philippines
Stachyris grammiceps	White-breasted Babbler	K*	Indonesia
Stachyris herberti	Sooty Babbler	K*	Laos
Micromacronus leytensis	Miniature Tit-babbler	K*	Philippines

Moupinia altirostris	Jerdon's Moupinia	K*	Burma, India, Pakistan
Turdoides hindei	Hinde's Pied Babbler	V	Kenya
Garrulax cinereifrons	Ashy-headed Laughingthrush	K*	Sri Lanka
Garrulax milleti	Black-hooded Laughingthrush	K*	Viet Nam
Garrulax maesi	Grey Laughingthrush	K*	China, Laos
Garrulax vassali	White-cheeked Laughingthrush	K*	Laos, Viet Nam
Garrulax galbanus	Yellow-throated Laughingthrush	K*	Bangladesh, China, India
Garrulax bieti	White-speckled Laughingthrush	K*	China
Garrulax cachinnans	Nilgiri Laughingthrush	K*	India
Garrulax yersini	Collared Laughingthrush	K*	Viet Nam
Garrulax formosus	Red-winged Laughingthrush	K*	China, Viet Nam
Liocichla omeiensis	Omei Shan Liocichla	K*	China
Alcippe variegaticeps	Gold-fronted Fulvetta	K*	China
Lioptilus gilberti	White-throated Mountain Babbler	R	Cameroon, Nigeria
Crocias langbianis	Grey-crowned Crocias	K*	Viet Nam
Crossleyia xanthophrys	Madagascar Yellowbrow	I	Madagascar
Paradoxornis ruficeps	Greater Rufous-headed Parrotbill	K*	Bhutan, Burma, China, India, Laos, Viet Nam
Paradoxornis flavirostris	Black-breasted Parrotbill	K*	India, Burma, China
Paradoxornis heudei	Eye-browed Parrotbill	I	China, U.S.S.R.
Picathartes gymnocephalus	White-necked Picathartes	V	West Africa
Picathartes oreas	Grey-necked Picathartes	R	Cameroon, Equatorial Guinea, Gabon, Nigeria
Polioptila lembeyei	Cuban Gnatcatcher	K*	Cuba
Bradypterus graueri	Grauer's Swamp Warbler	V	Burundi, Rwanda, Uganda, Zaire
Bradypterus grandis	Dja River Warbler	K	Cameroon, Gabon
Bradypterus major	Large-billed Bush Warbler	K*	China, India, Nepal, Pakistan
Bradypterus palliseri	Sri Lanka Bush Warbler	K*	Sri Lanka
Acrocephalus paludicola	Aquatic Warbler	K*	Western Palearctic, southern Africa
Acrocephalus sorghophilus	Speckled Warbler	K*	China
Acrocephalus rehsei	Nauru Warbler	K*	Nauru
Acrocephalus familiaris	Nihoa Warbler	R	Hawaiian Is (U.S.A.)
Acrocephalus rodericanus	Rodrigues Warbler	E	Rodrigues (Mauritius)
Acrocephalus sechellensis	Seychelles Warbler	R	Seychelles
Nesillas aldabranus	Aldabra Warbler	E	Aldabra (Seychelles)
Chloropeta gracilirostris	Papyrus Yellow Warbler	R	Burundi, Kenya, Rwanda, Uganda, Zaire, Zambia
Phylloscopus amoenus	Kolombangara Warbler	K*	Solomon Is
Cisticola haesitata	Socotra Cisticola	K*	Socotra (South Yemen)

Cisticola restricta	Tana River Cisticola	K	Kenya
Prinia fluviatilis	River Prinia	K	Cameroon, Chad, Nigeria
Prinia burnesi	Long-tailed Prinia	K*	India, Pakistan
Apalis chariessa	White-winged Apalis	K*	Kenya, Malawi, Mozambique, Tanzania
Apalis karamojae	Karamoja Apalis	K	Tanzania, Uganda
Apalis argentea	Kungwe Apalis	R	Burundi, Rwanda, Tanzania, Zaire
Apalis kaboboensis	Kabobo Apalis	R	Zaire
Apalis moreaui	Long-billed Apalis	R	Mozambique, Tanzania
Bathmocercus winifredae	Mrs Moreau's Warbler	R	Tanzania
Eremomela turneri	Turner's Eremomela	R	Kenya, Uganda, Zaire
Macrosphenus pulitzeri	Pulitzer's Longbill	I	Angola
Amaurocichla bocagii	Sao Tomé Short-tail	I	Sao Tomé
Chaetornis striatus	Bristled Grass Warbler	K*	India, Nepal
Megalurus pryeri	Marshland Warbler	K*	China, Japan
Megalurus albolimbatus	Fly River Grassbird	K*	Papua New Guinea
Cichlornis whitneyi	Whitney's Thicket Warbler	K*	Solomon Is, Vanuatu
Trichocichla rufa	Long-legged Warbler	E	Fiji
Malurus coronatus	Purple-crowned Fairy-wren	K*	Australia
Amytornis textilis	Thick-billed Grass-wren	K*	Australia
Amytornis goyderi	Eyrean Grass-wren	I	Australia
Amytornis barbatus	Grey Grass-wren	K*	Australia
Amytornis dorotheae	Carpentarian Grass-wren	K*	Australia
Dasyornis brachypterus	Eastern Bristlebird	K*	Australia
Dasyornis longirostris	Western Bristlebird	R	Australia
Aphelocephala pectoralis	Chestnut-breasted Whiteface	K*	Australia
Melaenornis annamarulae	Nimba Flycatcher	I	Ivory Coast, Liberia
Rhinomyias addita	Streaky-breasted Jungle-flycatcher	K*	Indonesia
Rhinomyias brunneata	Brown-chested Jungle-flycatcher	K*	China, India, Indonesia, Malaysia
Rhinomyias colonus	Henna-tailed Jungle-flycatcher	K*	Indonesia
Rhinomyias albigularis	White-throated Jungle-flycatcher	K*	Philippines
Rhinomyias insignis	White-browed Jungle-flycatcher	K*	Philippines
Ficedula bonthaina	Lompobattang Flycatcher	K*	Indonesia
Ficedula harterti	Sumba Flycatcher	K*	Indonesia
Ficedula crypta	Cryptic Flycatcher	K*	Philippines
Ficedula henrichi	Damar Blue Flycatcher	K*	Indonesia
Ficedula timorensis	Black-banded Flycatcher	K*	Indonesia
Cyornis sandfordi	Matinan Flycatcher	K*	Indonesia
Cyornis ruecki	Rueck's Blue Flycatcher	K*	Indonesia
Cyornis herioti	Blue-breasted Flycatcher	K*	Philippines

Muscicapa lendu	Chapin's Flycatcher	R	Kenya, Zaire, Uganda
Humblotia flavirostris	Grand Comoro Flycatcher	R	Comoro Is
Newtonia fanovanae	Red-tailed Newtonia	I	Madagascar
Petroica traversi	Chatham Island Black Robin	E	Chatham Is (New Zealand)
Platysteira laticincta	Banded Wattle-eye	E	Cameroon
Terpsiphone corvina	Seychelles Black Paradise-flycatcher	R	Seychelles
Eutrichomyias rowleyi	Caerulean Flycatcher	K*	Indonesia
Hypothymis helenae	Short-crested Monarch	K*	Philippines
Hypothymis coelestis	Celestial Monarch	K*	Philippines
Pomarea dimidiata	Rarotonga Flycatcher	V	Cook Is
Pomarea nigra	Tahiti Monarch	E	Society Is (France)
Pomarea mendozae	Marquesas Monarch	K*	Marquesas Is (France)
Mayrornis versicolor	Versicolour Flycatcher	K*	Fiji
Clytorhynchus hamlini	Rennell Shrikebill	K*	Solomon Is
Metabolus rugensis	Truk Monarch	R	Federated States of Micronesia (U.S.A.)
Monarcha everetti	White-tipped Monarch	K*	Indonesia
Monarcha boanensis	Black-chinned Monarch	K*	Indonesia
Monarcha sacerdotum	Flores Monarch	K*	Indonesia
Monarcha leucurus	White-tailed Monarch	K*	Indonesia
Monarcha brehmii	Biak Monarch	K*	Indonesia
Myiagra freycineti	Guam Flycatcher	K*	Guam (U.S.A.)
Myiagra atra	Biak Black Flycatcher	K*	Indonesia
Rhipidura superflua	Tawny-backed Fantail	K*	Indonesia
Rhipidura matthiae	St. Matthias Fantail	K*	Papua New Guinea
Pachycephala meyeri	Vogelkop Whistler	K*	Indonesia
Colluricincla sanghirensis	Sangihe Shrike-thrush	K*	Indonesia
Turnagra capensis	New Zealand Thrush	K*	New Zealand
Family Paridae			
Parus nuchalis	White-winged Tit	K*	India
Parus holsti	Yellow Tit	K*	Taiwan
Family Sittidae			
Sitta victoriae	White-browed Nuthatch	K*	Burma
Sitta whiteheadi	Corsican Nuthatch	K*	Corsica (France)
Sitta ledanti	Algerian Nuthatch	R	Algeria
Sitta yunnanensis	Black-masked Nuthatch	K*	China
Sitta solangiae	Yellow-billed Nuthatch	K*	Viet Nam

Sitta magna	Giant Nuthatch	K*	Burma, China, Thailand
Sitta formosa	Beautiful Nuthatch	K*	Bhutan, Burma, China, India, Laos, Viet Nam
Family Rhabdornithidae			
Rhabdornis grandis	Long-billed Rhabdornis	K*	Philippines
Family Dicaeidae			
Dicaeum everetti	Brown-backed Flowerpecker	K*	Indonesia, Malaysia
Dicaeum vincens	Legge's Flowerpecker	K*	Sri Lanka
Pardalotus quadragintus	Forty-spotted Pardalote	K*	Australia
Family Nectariniidae			
Anthreptes rubritorques	Banded Green Sunbird	R	Tanzania
Anthreptes pallidigaster	Amani Sunbird	R	Kenya, Tanzania
Dreptes thomensis	Giant Sunbird	K*	Sao Tomé
Nectarinia buettikoferi	Apricot-breasted Sunbird	K*	Indonesia
Nectarinia rockefelleri	Rockefeller's Sunbird	R	Zaire
Nectarinia prigoginei	Marungu Sunbird	E	Zaire
Nectarinia rufipennis	Rufous-winged Sunbird	R	Tanzania
Aethopyga duyvenbodei	Elegant Sunbird	K*	Indonesia
Family Zosteropidae			
Zosterops flava	Javan White-eye	K*	Indonesia, Malaysia
Zosterops meeki	Sudest White-eye	K*	Papua New Guinea
Zosterops kuehni	Ambon Yellow White-eye	K*	Indonesia
Zosterops luteirostris	Gezo White-eye	K*	Solomon Is
Zosterops sanctaecrucis	Nendo White-eye	K*	Solomon Is
Zosterops minuta	Small Lifou White-eye	K*	Loyalty Is (France)
Zosterops albogularis	White-breasted White-eye	E	Norfolk I. (Australia)
Zosterops inornata	Large Lifou White-eye	K*	Loyalty Is (France)
Zosterops modestus	Seychelles White-eye	E	Seychelles
Speirops brunneus	Fernando Po Speirops	R	Bioko (Equatorial Guinea)
Speirops leucophaeus	Principe Speirops	K*	Principe (Sao Tomé)
Zosterops mouroniensis	Mount Karthala White-eye	R	Comoro Is
Zosterops chloronothus	Mauritius Olive White-eye	V	Mauritius
Woodfordia lacertosa	Sanford's White-eye	K*	Solomon Is
Rukia ruki	Great Truk White-eye	E	Federated States of Micronesia (U.S.A.)

Rukia longirostra	Great Pohnpei White-eye	R	Federated States of Micronesia (U.S.A.)
Madanga ruficollis	Rufous-throated White-eye	K*	Indonesia
Lophozosterops dohertyi	Crested White-eye	K*	Indonesia
Oculocincta squamifrons	Pygmy White-eye	K*	Indonesia, Malaysia
Heleia muelleri	Spot-breasted White-eye	K*	Indonesia
Family Meliphagidae			
Myzomela kuehni	Crimson-hooded Honeyeater	K*	Indonesia
Meliphaga vicina	Sudest Meliphaga	K*	Papua New Guinea
Notiomystis cincta	Stitchbird	V	New Zealand
Philemon brassi	Brass's Friarbird	K*	Indonesia
Philemon fuscicapillus	Dusky Friarbird	K*	Indonesia
Philemon moluccensis	Black-faced Friarbird	K*	Indonesia
Melidectes princeps	Long-bearded Melidectes	K*	Indonesia, Papua New Guinea
Moho braccatus	Kauai Oo	E	Hawaiian Is (U.S.A.)
Moho bishopi	Bishop's Oo	K*	Hawaiian Is (U.S.A.)
Xanthomyza phrygia	Regent Honeyeater	K*	Australia
Manorina melanotis	Black-eared Miner	K*	Australia
Family Emberizidae			
Emberiza jankowskii	Jankowski's Bunting	K*	China, North Korea, U.S.S.R.
Emberiza sulphurata	Japanese Yellow Bunting	K*	China, Japan, Philippines, Taiwan
Ammodramus baileyi	Sierra Madre Sparrow	K*	Mexico
Torreornis inexpectata	Zapata Sparrow	R	Cuba
Melanodera melanodera	Black-throated Finch	K*	Argentina, Chile
Rowettia goughensis	Gough Bunting	R	Gough Island (U.K.)
Nesospiza acunhae	Tristan Bunting	R	Tristan da Cunha group (U.K.)
Nesospiza wilkinsi	Grosbeak Bunting	R	Tristan da Cunha group (U.K.)
Xenospingus concolor	Slender-billed Finch	K*	Chile, Peru
Incaspiza ortizi	Grey-winged Inca Finch	K*	Peru
Poospiza rubecula	Rufous-breasted Warbling Finch	K*	Peru
Poospiza garleppi	Cochabamba Mountain Finch	K*	Bolivia
Poospiza baeri	Tucuman Mountain Finch	K*	Argentina
Sporophila frontalis	Buffy-throated Seedeater	K*	Argentina, Brazil, Paraguay
Sporophila falcirostris	Temminck's Seedeater	K*	Argentina, Brazil
Sporophila insulata	Tumaco Seedeater	I	Colombia
Sporophila hypochroma	Rufous-rumped Seedeater	K*	Argentina, Bolivia
Sporophila ruficollis	Dark-throated Seedeater	K*	Argentina, Bolivia, Brazil, Paraguay, Uruguay

Sporophila cinnamomea	Chestnut Seedeater	K*	Argentina, Brazil, Paraguay
Sporophila melanogaster	Black-bellied Seedeater	K*	Brazil
Amaurospiza moesta	Blackish-blue Seedeater	K*	Argentina, Brazil
Camarhynchus pauper	Floreana Tree Finch	K*	Ecuador
Camarhynchus heliobates	Mangrove Finch	R	Ecuador
Atlapetes flaviceps	Olive-headed Brush Finch	I	Colombia
Atlapetes pallidiceps	Pale-headed Brush Finch	K*	Ecuador
Coryphaspiza melanotis	Black-masked Finch	K*	Argentina, Bolivia, Brazil, Paraguay
Gubernatrix cristata	Yellow Cardinal	K*	Argentina, Brazil, Uruguay
Saltator nigriceps	Black-cowled Saltator	K*	Ecuador, Peru
Saltator cinctus	Masked Saltator	K*	Ecuador
Conothraupis mesoleuca	Cone-billed Tanager	K*	Brazil
Chlorospingus flavovirens	Yellow-green Bush Tanager	K*	Colombia, Ecuador
Nemosia rourei	Cherry-throated Tanager	E	Brazil
Habia atrimaxillaris	Black-cheeked Ant Tanager	K*	Costa Rica
Habia gutturalis	Sooty Ant Tanager	K*	Colombia
Buthraupis melanochlamys	Black-and-gold Tanager	K*	Colombia
Buthraupis aureocincta	Gold-ringed Tanager	K*	Colombia
Buthraupis aureodorsalis	Golden-backed Mountain Tanager	K*	Peru
Euphonia chalybea	Green-throated Euphonia	K*	Argentina, Brazil, Paraguay
Chlorochrysa nitidissima	Multicoloured Tanager	K*	Colombia
Tangara cabanisi	Azure-rumped Tanager	I	Guatemala, Mexico
Tangara fastuosa	Seven-coloured Tanager	V	Brazil
Tangara peruviana	Black-backed Tanager	K*	Brazil
Tangara meyerdeschauenseei	Green-capped Tanager	K*	Peru
Dacnis albiventris	White-bellied Dacnis	K*	Brazil, Colombia, Ecuador, Peru, Venezuela
Dacnis hartlaubi	Turquoise Dacnis	K*	Colombia
Dacnis nigripes	Black-legged Dacnis	K*	Brazil
Dacnis berlepschi	Scarlet-breasted Dacnis	K*	Colombia, Ecuador
Diglossa venezuelensis	Venezuelan Flowerpiercer	K*	Venezuela
Family Parulidae			
Vermivora bachmanii	Bachman's Warbler	E	Cuba, U.S.A.
Dendroica chrysoparia	Golden-cheeked Warbler	K*	U.S.A., Central America
Dendroica kirtlandii	Kirtland's Warbler	E	Bahama Is, U.S.A.
Catharopeza bishopi	Whistling Warbler	K*	St. Vincent
Geothlypis flavovelata	Altamira Yellowthroat	K*	Mexico
Geothlypis speciosa	Black-polled Yellowthroat	K*	Mexico

Leucopeza semperi	Semper's Warbler	E	St. Lucia
Myioborus pariae	Yellow-faced Redstart	K*	Venezuela
Basileuterus cinereicollis	Grey-throated Warbler	K*	Colombia, Venezuela
Basileuterus ignotus	Pirre Warbler	K*	Panama
Basileuterus griseiceps	Grey-headed Warbler	K*	Venezuela
Basileuterus leucophrys	White-striped Warbler	K*	Brazil
Xenoligea montana	White-winged Ground Warbler	K*	Dominican Republic, Haiti
Conirostrum margaritae	Pearly-breasted Conebill	K*	Brazil, Peru
Family Drepanididae			
Oreomystis bairdi	Kauai Creeper	K*	Hawaiian Is (U.S.A.)
Oreomystis mana	Hawaii Creeper	K*	Hawaiian Is (U.S.A.)
Paroreomyza maculata	Oahu Creeper	K*	Hawaiian Is (U.S.A.)
Paroreomyza flammea	Mulokai Creeper	K*	Hawaiian Is (U.S.A.)
Paroreomyza montana	Maui Creeper	K*	Hawaiian Is (U.S.A.)
Loxops coccinea	Akepa	K*	Hawaiian Is (U.S.A.)
Hemignathus obscurus	Akialoa	E	Hawaiian Is (U.S.A.)
Hemignathus lucidus	Nukupuu	E	Hawaiian Is (U.S.A.)
Hemignathus munroi	Akiapolaau	E	Hawaiian Is (U.S.A.)
Pseudonestor xanthophrys	Maui Parrotbill	V	Hawaiian Is (U.S.A.)
Telespyza ultima	Nihoa Finch	K*	Hawaiian Is (U.S.A.)
Telespyza cantans	Laysan Finch	K*	Hawaiian Is (U.S.A.)
Psittirostra psittacea	Ou	E	Hawaiian Is (U.S.A.)
Psittirostra bailleui	Palila	E	Hawaiian Is (U.S.A.)
Melamprosops phaesoma	Poo Uli	R	Hawaiian Is (U.S.A.)
Palmeria dolei	Crested Honeycreeper	V	Hawaiian Is (U.S.A.)
Family Vireonidae			
Vireo atricapillus	Black-capped Vireo	K*	Mexico, U.S.A.
Vireo caribaeus	San Andres Vireo	K*	San Andres I. (Colombia)
Family Icteridae			
Psarocolius cassini	Chestnut-mantled Oropendola	K*	Colombia
Cacicus koepckeae	Selva Cacique	K*	Peru
Icterus bonana	Martinique Oriole	K*	Martinique (France)
Icterus oberi	Montserrat Oriole	K*	Montserrat (U.K.)
Agelaius flavus	Saffron-cowled Blackbird	K*	Argentina, Bolivia, Brazil, Paraguay, Uruguay

Agelaius xanthomus	Yellow-shouldered Blackbird	V	Puerto Rico
Sturnella defilippi	Lesser Red-breasted Meadowlark	K*	Argentina, Brazil, Uruguay
Hypopyrrhus pyrohypogaster	Red-bellied Grackle	K*	Colombia
Curaeus forbesi	Forbes's Blackbird	K*	Brazil
Family Fringillidae			
Fringilla teydea	Blue Chaffinch	R	Canary Is (Spain)
Serinus ankoberensis	Ankober Serin	R	Ethiopia
Serinus flavigula	Yellow-throated Serin	I	Ethiopia
Neospiza concolor	Sao Tomé Grosbeak	I	Sao Tomé
Carduelis yarrellii	Yellow-faced Siskin	K*	Brazil, Venezuela
Carduelis cucullata	Red Siskin	E	Venezuela
Carduelis siemiradzkii	Saffron Siskin	K*	Ecuador
Acanthis johannis	Warsangli Linnet	R	Somalia
Family Estrildidae			
Estrilda poliopareia	Anambra Waxbill	K	Nigeria
Estrilda nigriloris	Black-lored Waxbill	K	Zaire
Estrilda formosa	Green Munia	K*	India
Erythrura viridifacies	Green-faced Parrotfinch	K*	Philippines
Erythrura coloria	Red-eared Parrotfinch	K*	Philippines
Erythrura kleinschmidti	Pink-billed Parrotfinch	R	Fiji
Erythrura gouldiae	Gouldian Finch	K*	Australia
Padda fuscata	Timor Sparrow	K*	Indonesia
Family Ploceidae			
Ploceus bannermani	Bannerman's Weaver	V	Cameroon, Nigeria
Ploceus batesi	Bates's Weaver	R	Cameroon
Ploceus nigrimentum	Black-chinned Weaver	K	Angola, Congo
Ploceus subpersonatus	Loango Slender-billed Weaver	K	Angola, Congo, Zaire
Ploceus ruweti	Lake Lufira Weaver	K	Zaire
Ploceus golandi	Clarke's Weaver	E	Kenya
Ploceus aureonucha	Golden-naped Weaver	R	Zaire
Ploceus megarhynchus	Finn's Baya Weaver	K*	India
Ploceus flavipes	Yellow-legged Weaver	R	Zaire
Ploceus nicolli	Tanzanian Mountain Weaver	R	Tanzania
Ploceus victoriae	Entebbe Weaver	K*	Uganda
Malimbus ibadanensis	Ibadan Malimbe	E	Nigeria
Malimbus ballmanni	Gola Malimbe	I	Liberia, Sierra Leone

Foudia rubra	Mauritius Fody	E	Mauritius
Foudia sechellarum	Seychelles Fody	R	Seychelles
Foudia flavicans	Rodrigues Fody	E	Rodrigues (Mauritius)
Family Sturnidae			
Aplonis zelandica	Rusty-winged Starling	K*	Solomon Is, Vanuatu
Aplonis santovestris	Santo Mountain Starling	R	Vanuatu
Aplonis pelzelni	Pohnpei Mountain Starling	K*	Federated States of Micronesia (U.S.A.)
Aplonis cinerascens	Rarotonga Starling	K*	Cook Is
Cinnyricinclus femoralis	Abbott's Starling	K*	Kenya, Tanzania
Sturnus senex	Sri Lanka White-headed Myna	K*	Sri Lanka
Leucopsar rothschildi	Bali Starling	E	Indonesia
Family Oriolidae			
Oriolus isabeliae	Isabela Oriole	K*	Philippines
Oriolus mellianus	Silver Oriole	K*	China, Thailand
Dicrurus modestus	Principe Drongo	K*	Principe (Sao Tomé)
Dicrurus fuscipennis	Grand Comoro Drongo	R	Comoro Is
Dicrurus waldeni	Mayotte Drongo	R	Mayotte (France)
Family Callaeidae			
Callaeas cinerea	South Island Kokako	E	New Zealand
Creadion carunculatus	Saddleback	K*	New Zealand
Family Cracticidae			
Cracticus louisiadensis	Sudest Butcherbird	K*	Papua New Guinea
Family Ptilonorhynchidae			
Sericulus bakeri	Adelbert Bowerbird	K*	Papua New Guinea
Family Paradisaeidae			
Macregoria pulchra	Macgregor's Bird of Paradise	K*	Indonesia, Papua New Guinea
Paradigalla carunculata	Long-tailed Paradigalla	K*	Indonesia
Epimachus fastuosus	Black Sicklebill	K*	Indonesia, Papua New Guinea
Epimachus meyeri	Brown Sicklebill	K*	Indonesia, Papua New Guinea
Astrapia mayeri	Ribbon-tailed Astrapia	K*	Indonesia, Papua New Guinea

Parotia wahnesi	Wahnes's Parotia	K*	Papua New Guinea
Paradisaea decora	Goldie's Bird of Paradise	K*	Papua New Guinea
Paradisaea rudolphi	Blue Bird of Paradise	K*	Papua New Guinea
Family Corvidae			
Cyanolyca pulchra	Beautiful Jay	K*	Colombia, Ecuador
Cyanolyca nana	Dwarf Jay	K*	Mexico
Cyanolyca mirabilis	White-throated Jay	K*	Mexico
Cyanocorax caeruleus	Azure Jay	K*	Argentina, Brazil
Perisoreus internigrans	Sichuan Jay	K*	China
Urocissa ornata	Sri Lanka Magpie	K*	Sri Lanka
Crypsirina cucullata	Hooded Treepie	K*	Burma
Temnurus temnurus	Ratchet-tailed Treepie	K*	China, Viet Nam
Zavattariornis stresemanni	Ethiopian Bush Crow	R	Ethiopia
Corvus unicolor	Banggai Crow	K*	Indonesia
Corvus florensis	Flores Crow	K*	Indonesia
Corvus kubaryi	Marianas Crow	E	Guam, Northern Mariana Is (U.S.A.)
Corvus tropicus	Hawaiian Crow	E	Hawaiian Is (U.S.A.)

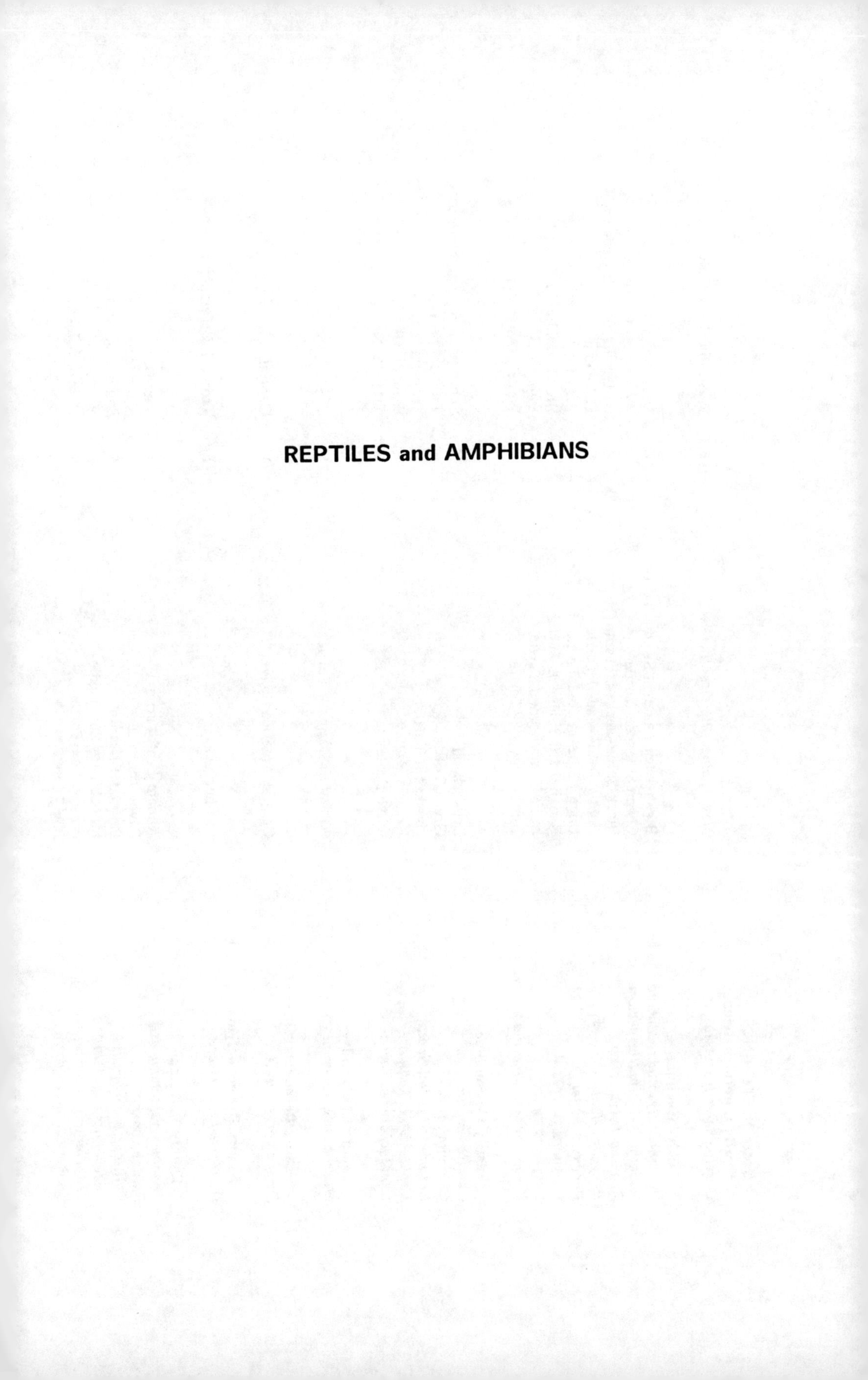

REPTILES and AMPHIBIANS

CLASS REPTILIA

Order TESTUDINES			
Family Carettochelyidae			
Carettochelys insculpta	New Guinea Plateless Turtle	K	Australia, New Guinea
Family Chelidae			
Acanthochelys macrocephala	Big-headed Pantanal Swamp Turtle	K	Brazil
Acanthochelys pallidipectoris	Chaco Sideneck Turtle	R	Argentina, Paraguay
Acanthochelys spixii	Black Spine-necked Swamp Turtle	K	Argentina, Brazil, Uruguay
Phrynops dahli	Dahl's Toad-headed Turtle	I	Colombia
Phrynops hogei	Hoge's Side-necked Turtle	I	Brazil
Phrynops rufipes	Red-headed Sideneck Turtle	K	Brazil, Colombia
Phrynops zuliae	Zulia Toad-headed Turtle	K	Venezuela
Pseudemydura umbrina	Western Swamp Turtle	E	Western Australia
Family Cheloniidae			
Caretta caretta	Loggerhead Turtle	V	Subtropical & Temperate Seas
Chelonia mydas	Green Turtle	E	Tropical Seas
Eretmochelys imbricata	Hawksbill Turtle	E	Tropical Seas
Lepidochelys kempii	Kemp's Ridley	E	Gulf of Mexico
Lepidochelys olivacea	Olive Ridley	E	Tropical Seas
Family Chelydridae			
Macroclemys temminckii	Alligator Snapping Turtle	V	U.S.A.
Family Dermatemydidae			
Dermatemys mawii	Central American River Turtle	V	Central America
Family Dermochelyidae			
Dermochelys coriacea	Leatherback	E	Tropical & Temperate Seas
Family Emydidae			
Annamemys annamensis	Annam Leaf Turtle	K	Viet Nam
Batagur baska	River Terrapin	E	South-east Asia
Callagur borneoensis	Painted Terrapin	E	South-east Asia
Cistoclemmys galbinifrons	Indochinese Box Turtle	K	Viet Nam
Cistoclemmys hainanensis	Hainan Box Turtle	K	Hainan (China)
Clemmys muhlenbergii	Bog Turtle	R	U.S.A.

Cuora yunnanensis	Yunnan Box Turtle	K	China
Geoclemys hamiltonii	Spotted Pond Turtle	I	South Asia
Graptemys barbouri	Barbour's Map Turtle	K	U.S.A.
Graptemys caglei	Cagle's Map Turtle	K	U.S.A.
Graptemys flavimaculata	Yellow-blotched Map Turtle	I	U.S.A.
Graptemys oculifera	Ringed Map Turtle	K	U.S.A.
Heosemys depressa	Arakan Forest Turtle	K	Burma
Heosemys leytensis	Leyte Pond Turtle	I	Leyte (Philippines)
Geoemyda silvatica	Cane Turtle	V	India
Heosemys spinosa	Spiny Turtle	K	Indonesia, Malaysia, Thailand
Kachuga kachuga	Red-crowned Roofed Turtle	I	Bangladesh, India, Nepal
Kachuga sylhetensis	Assam Roofed Turtle	K	India
Kachuga trivittata	Burmese Roofed Turtle	K	Burma
Melanochelys tricarinata	Tricarinate Hill Turtle	I	Bangladesh, India, Nepal
Morenia ocellata	Burmese Eyed Turtle	K	Burma
Orlitia borneensis	Malaysian Giant Turtle	K	Indonesia, Malaysia
Pseudemys alabamensis	Alabama Red-bellied Turtle	R	U.S.A.
Trachemys terrapen felis	Cat Island Turtle	R	Bahamas
Trachemys stejnegeri malonei	Inagua Island Turtle	R	Bahamas
Trachemys scripta callirostris	South American Red-lined Turtle	V	Colombia, Venezuela
Rhinoclemmys rubida	Mexican Spotted Wood Turtle	K	Mexico
Terrapene coahuila	Aquatic Box Turtle	V	Mexico
Terrapene nelsoni	Spotted Box Turtle	K	Mexico
Trachemys decorata	Hispaniolan Slider	K	Hispaniola
Family Kinosternidae			
Kinosternon angustipons	Narrow-bridged Mud Turtle	R	Costa Rica, Nicaragua, Panama
Kinosternon creaseri	Creaser's Mud Turtle	V	Mexico
Kinosternon dunni	Dunn's Mud Turtle	R	Colombia
Kinosternon oaxacae	Oaxaca Mud Turtle	I	Mexico
Sternotherus depressus	Flattened Musk Turtle	V	U.S.A.
Family Pelomedusidae			
Erymnochelys madagascariensis	Madagascan Side-necked Turtle	I	Madagascar
Pelusios seychellensis	Seychelles Mud Turtle	K	Seychelles
Podocnemis erythrocephala	Red-headed Amazon Turtle	K	Brazil, Venezuela
Podocnemis expansa	South American River Turtle	E	Amazon Basin
Podocnemis lewyana	Rio Magdalena River Turtle	I	Colombia
Podocnemis sextuberculata		K	Brazil, Colombia, Peru
Podocnemis unifilis	Yellow-spotted Sideneck Turtle	V	Amazon Basin

Family Testudinidae			
Geochelone chilensis	Chaco Tortoise	V	Argentina, Paraguay
Geochelone elephantopus	Galapagos Giant Tortoise	V	Galapagos Is
Geochelone gigantea	Aldabra Giant Tortoise	R	Aldabra
Geochelone platynota	Burmese Starred Tortoise	K	Burma
Geochelone radiata	Radiated Tortoise	V	Madagascar
Geochelone yniphora	Angonoka	E	Madagascar
Gopherus agassizii	Desert Tortoise	V	Mexico, U.S.A.
Gopherus berlandieri	Texas Gopher Tortoise	I	Mexico, U.S.A.
Gopherus flavomarginatus	Bolson Tortoise	E	Mexico
Gopherus polyphemus	Florida Gopher Tortoise	V	U.S.A.
Homopus bergeri	Berger's Tortoise	K	Namibia
Indotestudo elongata	Elongated Tortoise	K	India, South-east Asia
Indotestudo forstenii	Travancore Tortoise	R	India, Indonesia*
Malacochersus tornieri	Pancake Tortoise	K	Kenya, Tanzania
Manouria emys	Burmese Brown Tortoise	K	South-east Asia
Manouria impressa	Impressed Tortoise	K	South-east Asia
Psammobates geometricus	Geometric Tortoise	V	South Africa
Pyxis arachnoides	Spider Tortoise	I	Madagascar
Pyxis planicauda	Madagascar Flat-shelled Tortoise	I	Madagascar
Testudo graeca graeca	Spur-thighed Tortoise	V	Europe, North Africa
Testudo hermanni	Hermann's Tortoise	V	Europe
Testudo kleinmanni	Egyptian Tortoise	V	Egypt, Israel, Libya
Family Trionychidae			
Trionyx nigricans	Black Soft-shell Turtle	R	Bangladesh
Order CROCODYLIA			
Family Alligatoridae			
Alligator sinensis	Chinese Alligator	E	China
Caiman crocodilus	Spectacled Caiman	T	Central & South America
Caiman latirostris	Broad-nosed Caiman	E	Southern South America
Melanosuchus niger	Black Caiman	E	South America
Family Crocodylidae			
Crocodylus acutus	American Crocodile	E	Caribbean, Central America, U.S.A.
Crocodylus cataphractus	African Slender-snouted Crocodile	I	Africa
Crocodylus intermedius	Orinoco Crocodile	E	Colombia, Venezuela
Crocodylus johnsoni	Australian Fresh-water Crocodile	V	Australia

Crocodylus mindorensis	Philippines Crocodile	E	Philippines
Crocodylus moreletii	Morelet's Crocodile	E	Central America
Crocodylus niloticus	Nile Crocodile	V	Africa, Madagascar
Crocodylus novaeguineae	New Guinea Crocodile	V	New Guinea
Crocodylus palustris	Mugger	V	South Asia
Crocodylus porosus	Estuarine Crocodile	E	Asia, Australia, West Pacific
Crocodylus rhombifer	Cuban Crocodile	E	Cuba
Crocodylus siamensis	Siamese Crocodile	E	South-east Asia
Osteolaemus tetraspis	West African Dwarf Crocodile	I	West & Central Africa
Tomistoma schlegelii	False Gharial	E	South-east Asia
Family Gavialidae			
Gavialis gangeticus	Gharial	E	South Asia
Order RHYNCHOCEPHALIA			
Family Sphenodontidae			
Sphenodon punctatus	Tuatara	R	New Zealand
Order SAURIA			
Family Agamidae			
Ceratophora tennentii	Leaf-nosed Lizard	V	Sri Lanka
Hydrosaurus pustulatus	Sail-fin Lizard	V	Philippines
Family Anguidae			
Gerrhonotus panamintus	Panamint Alligator Lizard	K	U.S.A.
Family Anniellidae			
Anniella pulchra nigra	Black Legless Lizard	I	U.S.A.
Family Chamaeleonidae			
Bradypodion taeniabronchum	Smith's Dwarf Chamaeleon	V	South Africa
Family Gekkonidae			
Anarbylus switaki	Switak's Barefoot Gecko	R	U.S.A.
Nactus serpensinsula	Serpent Island Gecko	R	Round I., Serpent I.
Oedura reticulata	Reticulated Velvet Gecko	V	Australia
Phelsuma edwardnewtonii	Rodrigues Day Gecko	E	Rodrigues
Phelsuma guentheri	Gunther's Gecko	E	Round I.

Species	Common name	Status	Distribution
Family Helodermatidae			
Heloderma horridum	Beaded Lizard	I	Guatemala, Mexico
Heloderma suspectum	Gila Monster	V	Mexico, U.S.A.
Family Iguanidae			
Amblyrhynchus cristatus	Galapagos Marine Iguana	R	Galapagos Is
Anolis roosevelti	Culebra Island Giant Anole	E	Culebra I. (Puerto Rico)
Brachylophus fasciatus	South Pacific Banded Iguana	V	Fiji, Tonga
Brachylophus vitiensis	Fiji Crested Iguana	V	Fiji
Conolophus pallidus	Barrington Land Iguana	R	Galapagos Is
Conolophus subcristatus	Galapagos Land Iguana	V	Galapagos Is
Cyclura carinata	Turks & Caicos Rock Iguana	R	Bahamas, Turks & Caicos
Cyclura cornuta	Rhinoceros Rock Iguana	T	Hispaniola, Mona I.
Cyclura cychlura	Andros Ground Iguana	R	Bahamas
Cyclura nubila	Cuban Ground Iguana	V	Cayman Is, Cuba
Cyclura pinguis	Anegada Ground Iguana	E	Anegada (British Virgin Is)
Cyclura ricordii	Hispaniolan Ground Iguana	I	Hispaniola
Cyclura rileyi		T	Bahamas
Gambelia silus	San Joaquin Leopard Lizard	E	U.S.A.
Phrynosoma cornatum blainvillei	San Diego Horned Lizard	K	Mexico, U.S.A.
Uma inornata	Coachella Fringe-toed Lizard	V	U.S.A.
Family Lacertidae			
Gallotia simonyi	Hierro Giant Lizard	E	Hierro (Canary Is)
Podarcis filfolensis filfolensis	Filfola Lizard	R	Filfola I. (Malta)
Family Scincidae			
Ctenotus lancelini	Lancelin Island Skink	R	Australia
Gongylomorphus bojerii fontenayi	Macabé Forest Skink	R	Mauritius
Leiolopisma telfairii	Round Island Skink	R	Round I.
Macroscincus coctaei	Cape Verde Giant Skink	Ex?	Cape Verde Is
Pseudemoia palfreymani	Pedra Branca Skink	R	Pedra Branca I. (Australia)
Tiliqua adelaidensis	Adelaide Pigmy Bluetongue Lizard	I	Australia
Tribolonotus ponceleti		I	Shortland I. (Solomon Is)
Family Teiidae			
Ameiva polops	St Croix Ground Lizard	E	U.S. Virgin Is
Cnemidophorus hyperythrus	Orange-throated Whiptail	V	Mexico, U.S.A.

Family Varanidae			
Varanus grayi	Gray's Monitor	R	Luzon (Philippines)
Varanus griseus caspius	Central Asian Monitor	V	Central-west Asia
Varanus komodoensis	Komodo Dragon	R	Indonesia
Family Xantusiidae			
Xantusia riversiana	Island Night Lizard	R	U.S.A.
Order SERPENTES			
Family Aniliidae			
Anomochilus leonardi	Leonard's Pipe Snake	K	Peninsular Malaysia
Family Boidae			
Acrantophis dumerili		K	Madagascar
Acrantophis madagascariensis	Madagascar Boa	K	Madagascar
Bolyeria multocarinata	Round Island Boa	E	Round I.
Casarea dussumieri	Round Island Keel-scaled Boa	E	Round I.
Charina bottae umbratica	Southern Rubber Boa	R	U.S.A.
Epicrates angulifer	Cuban Tree Boa	I	Cuba
Epicrates inornatus	Puerto Rican Boa	E	Puerto Rico
Epicrates monensis monensis	Mona Boa	R	Mona I.
Epicrates striatus fosteri	Bimini Boa	R	Bahamas
Epicrates subflavus	Jamaican Boa	V	Jamaica
Python molurus	Indian Python	V	South & South-east Asia
Sanzinia madagascariensis		K	Madagascar
Family Colubridae			
Drymarchon corais couperi	Eastern Indigo Snake	V	U.S.A.
Iguanognathus werneri		I	Sumatra
Masticophis flagellum ruddocki	San Joaquin Coachwhip	R	U.S.A.
Masticophis lateralis euryxanthus	Almeda Striped Racer	R	U.S.A.
Nerodia fasciata taeniata	Atlantic Saltmarsh Snake	R	U.S.A.
Nerodia harteri paucimaculata	Concho Water Snake	V	U.S.A.
Nerodia sipedon insularum	Lake Erie Water Snake	K	U.S.A.
Thamnophis gigas	Giant Garter Snake	R	U.S.A.
Thamnophis hammondi	Two-striped Garter Snake	R	Mexico, U.S.A.
Thamnophis sirtalis tetrataenia	San Francisco Garter Snake	E	U.S.A.
Thermophis baileyi		R	China

Family Elapidae			
Brachyaspis atriceps		R	Australia
Hoplocephalus bungaroides	Broad-headed Snake	I	Australia
Naja oxiana	Central Asian Cobra	E	Central Asia
Ogmodon vitianus	Fiji Snake (Bolo)	I	Fiji
Family Hydrophiidae			
Laticauda crockeri		R	Rennel I. (Solomon Is)
Family Typhlopidae			
Typhlops monensis	Mona Blind Snake	R	Mona I.
Family Viperidae			
Bothrops insularis	Queimada Island Bothrops	R	Queimada I. (Brazil)
Crotalus unicolor	Aruba Island Rattlesnake	R	Aruba I.
Crotalus willardi	Ridge-nosed Rattlesnake	T	Mexico, U.S.A.
Vipera ammodytes transcaucasiana	Transcaucasian Long-nosed Viper	R	Turkey, U.S.S.R.
Vipera bornmuelleri		I	Lebanon, Syria
Vipera bulgardaghica		I	Turkey
Vipera kaznakovi	Caucasian Viper	R	Turkey, U.S.S.R.
Vipera latifii	Latifi's Viper	E	Iran
Vipera lebetina schweizeri	Lebetine Viper	V	Cyclades Is (Greece)
Vipera raddei	Armenian Viper	I	Iran, Turkey, U.S.S.R.
Vipera wagneri		I	Iran

CLASS AMPHIBIA

Order ANURA

Family Bufonidae			
Bufo boreas nelsoni	Amargosa Toad	I	U.S.A.
Bufo exsul	Black Toad	R	U.S.A.
Bufo houstonensis	Houston Toad	E	U.S.A.
Bufo periglenes	Golden Toad	E	Costa Rica
Bufo retiformis	Sonoran Green Toad	V	Mexico, U.S.A.
Nectophrynoides occidentalis	Mount Nimba Viviparous Toad	V	Guinea, Ivory Coast
Family Discoglossidae			
Discoglossus nigriventer	Israel Painted Frog	Ex?	Israel
Alytes muletensis	Ferreret	I	Mallorca (Spain)
Family Hylidae			
Hyla andersoni	Pine Barrens Tree Frog	R	U.S.A.
Pseudacris streckeri illinoensis	Illinois Chorus Frog	I	U.S.A.
Family Hyperoliidae			
Tachycnemis seychellensis	Seychelles Tree Frog	R	Seychelles
Family Leiopelmatidae			
Leiopelma archeyi	Archey's Frog	R	New Zealand
Leiopelma hamiltoni	Hamilton's Frog	R	New Zealand
Leiopelma hochstetteri	Hochstetter's Frog	R	New Zealand
Family Leptodactylidae			
Batrachophrynus macrostomus	Lake Junin Giant Frog	K	Peru
Eleutherodactylus jasperi	Golden Cocqui Frog	R	Puerto Rico
Somuncuria somuncurensis		I	Argentina
Family Microhylidae			
Melanobatrachus indicus	Black Microhylid	I	India
Family Myobatrachidae			
Philoria frosti	Baw Baw Frog	I	Australia
Rheobatrachus silus	Conondale Gastric-brooding Frog	E	Australia
Rheobatrachus vitellinus	Eungella Gastric-brooding Frog	I	Australia

Family Pelobatidae			
Pelobates fuscus insubricus	Italian Spadefoot Toad	E	Italy
Family Pipidae			
Xenopus gilli	Cape Platanna	V	South Africa
Family Ranidae			
Conraua goliath	Goliath Frog	V	Cameroon, Eq. Guinea
Nesomantis thomasseti	Thomasset's Seychelles Frog	R	Seychelles
Platymantis vitianus	Fijian Ground Frog	K	Fiji
Rana latastei	Italian Agile Frog	V	Italy, Switzerland, Yugoslavia
Rana fisheri	Vegas Valley Leopard Frog	E	U.S.A.
Sooglossus gardineri	Gardiner's Seychelles Frog	R	Seychelles
Sooglossus sechellensis	Seychelles Frog	R	Seychelles
Order CAUDATA			
Family Ambystomatidae			
Ambystoma tigrinum californiense	California Tiger Salamander	V	U.S.A.
Ambystoma dumerilii dumerilii	Lake Patzcuaro Salamander	R	Mexico
Ambystoma lermaensis	Lake Lerma Salamander	R	Mexico
Ambystoma macrodactylum croceum	Santa Cruz Long-toed Salamander	E	U.S.A.
Ambystoma mexicanum	Axolotl	R	Mexico
Family Cryptobranchidae			
Andrias davidianus	Chinese Giant Salamander	I	China
Andrias japonicus	Japanese Giant Salamander	R	Japan
Family Hynobiidae			
Batrachuperus mustersi		K	Afghanistan
Family Plethondontidae			
Batrachoseps aridus	Desert Slender Salamander	E	U.S.A.
Batrachoseps simatus	Kern Canyon Slender Salamander	R	U.S.A.
Batrachoseps stebbinsi	Tehachapi Slender Salamander	R	U.S.A.
Eurycea nana	San Marcos Salamander	R	U.S.A.
Hydromantes brunus	Limestone Salamander	R	U.S.A.
Hydromantes shastae	Shasta Salamander	R	U.S.A.
Phaeognathus hubrichti	Red Hills Salamander	R	U.S.A.

Plethodon larselli	Larch Mountain Salamander	I	U.S.A.
Plethodon neomexicanus	Jemez Mountains Salamander	V	U.S.A.
Plethodon nettingi	Cheat Mountain Salamander	K	U.S.A.
Plethodon stormi	Siskiyou Mountains Salamander	K	U.S.A.
Typhlomolge rathbuni	Texas Blind Salamander	E	U.S.A.
Typhlotriton spelaeus	Grotto Salamander	K	U.S.A.
Family Proteidae			
Proteus anguinus	Olm	V	Italy, Yugoslavia
Family Salamandridae			
Chioglossa lusitanica	Gold-striped Salamander	V	Portugal, Spain
Paramesotriton deloustali	Vietnamese Salamander	I	Viet Nam

FISH

Species	Common name	Status	Distribution
CLASS CEPHALASPIDOMORPHI			
Order PETROMYZONTIFORMES			
Family Petromyzontidae			
Lampetra minima	Miller Lake Lamprey	Ex	[U.S.A.]
Mordacia praecox	Non-parasitic Lamprey	R	Australia
CLASS OSTEICHTHYES			
Order COELACANTHIFORMES			
Family Latimeriidae			
Latimeria chalumnae	Latimeria	K	Comoros, [South Africa]
Order ACIPENSERIFORMES			
Family Acipenseridae			
Acipenser brevirostrum	Shortnose Sturgeon	V	Ca ada, U.S.A.
Acipenser fulvescens	Lake Sturgeon	V	Canada, U.S.A.
Acipenser oxyrhynchus	Atlantic Sturgeon	V	Canada, U.S.A.
Acipenser schrencki	Amur Sturgeon	V	U.S.S.R.
Acipenser sturio	Common Sturgeon	E	Europe
Huso dauricus	Kaluga	R	U.S.S.R.
Scaphirhynchus albus	Pallid Sturgeon	E	U.S.A.
Family Polyodontidae			
Polyodon spathula	Paddlefish	I	U.S.A.
Order OSTEOGLOSSIFORMES			
Family Osteoglossidae			
Arapaima gigas	Pirarucu	V	Amazon Basin
Scleropages formosus	Asian Bonytongue	K	South-east Asia
Family Notopteridae			
Notopterus blanci	Featherback	R	Kampuchea, Thailand
Order CYPRINIFORMES			
Family Cyprinidae			
Acanthorutilus handlirschi	Ciçek	E	Turkey
Balantiocheilus melanopterus	Pla Hang Mai	I	South-east Asia
Barbus andrewi	Cape Whitefish	V	South Africa
Barbus burchelli	Burchell's Redfin	R	South Africa

Barbus burgi	Berg River Redfin	E	South Africa
Barbus calidus	Clanwilliam Redfin	R	South Africa
Barbus capensis	Clanwilliam Yellowfish	R	South Africa
Barbus cumingi	Cuming's Two-banded Barb	V	Sri Lanka
Barbus erubescens	Twee River Redfin	V	South Africa
Barbus halei		I	Thailand, Malaysia
Barbus hospes	Namaqua Barb	R	South Africa
Barbus nigrofasciatus	Black Ruby Barb	V	Sri Lanka
Barbus phlegethon	Fiery Redfin	E	South Africa
Barbus pleurotaenia	Side Striped Barb	V	Sri Lanka
Barbus serra	Sawfin	V	South Africa
Barbus somphongsi		I	Thailand
Barbus srilankensis		E	Sri Lanka
Barbus tenuis	Slender Redfin	R	South Africa
Barbus titteya	Cherry Barb	V	Sri Lanka
Barbus treurensis	Treur River Barb	V	South Africa
Barbus trevelyani	Border Barb	V	South Africa
Chela caeruleostigmata		R	Thailand
Dionda diaboli	Devil's River Minnow	V	Mexico, U.S.A.
Dionda dichroma	Bicolor Minnow	R	Mexico
Dionda mandibularis	Flatjaw Minnow	E	Mexico
Eremichthys acros	Desert Dace	V	U.S.A.
Evarra bustamantei		Ex	[Mexico]
Evarra eigenmanni		Ex	[Mexico]
Evarra tlahuacensis		Ex	[Mexico]
Gila alvordensis	Alvord Chub	V	U.S.A.
Gila bicolor (subspecies)	Tui Chub	T*	U.S.A.
Gila boraxobius	Borax Lake Chub	V	U.S.A.
Gila crassicauda	Thicktail Chub	Ex	[U.S.A.]
Gila cypha	Humpback Chub	E	U.S.A.
Gila ditaenia	Sonora Chub	V	Mexico, U.S.A.
Gila elegans	Bonytail	E	U.S.A.
Gila intermedia	Gila Chub	V	U.S.A.
Gila modesta	Saltillo Chub	V	Mexico
Gila nigrescens	Chihuahuan Chub	V	Mexico, U.S.A.
Gila purpurea	Yaqui Chub	V	Mexico, U.S.A.
Gila robusta	Roundtail Chub	V	U.S.A.
Hemitremia flammea	Flame Chub	R	U.S.A.
Hybopsis cahni	Slender Chub	V	U.S.A.

Hybopsis crameri	Oregon Chub	R	U.S.A.
Hybopsis labrosa	Thicklip Chub	R	U.S.A.
Hybopsis monacha	Spotfin Chub	E	U.S.A.
Iotichthys phlegethontis	Least Chub	V	U.S.A.
Labeo fisheri	Green Labeo	E	Sri Lanka
Labeo seeberi	Clanwilliam Sandfish	R	South Africa
Lepidomeda albivallis	White River Spinedace	E	U.S.A.
Lepidomeda altivelis	Pahranagat Spinedace	Ex	[U.S.A.]
Lepidomeda mollispinis	Virgin Spinedace	V	U.S.A.
Lepidomeda vittata	Little Colorado Spinedace	V	U.S.A.
Meda fulgida	Spikedace	V	U.S.A.
Moapa coriacea	Moapa Dace	V	U.S.A.
Notropis aguirrepequenoi	Pilon Shiner	V	Mexico
Notropis bocagrande	Bigmouth Shiner	V	Mexico
Notropis caeruleus	Blue Shiner	V	U.S.A.
Notropis callitaenia	Bluestripe Shiner	V	U.S.A.
Notropis formosus	Beautiful Shiner	V	Mexico, U.S.A.
Notropis hubbsi	Bluehead Shiner	R	U.S.A.
Notropis jemezanus	Rio Grande Shiner	I	U.S.A.
Notropis mekistocholas	Cape Fear Shiner	V	U.S.A.
Notropis orca	Phantom Shiner	Ex	[Mexico, U.S.A.]
Notropis perpallidus	Peppered Shiner	V	U.S.A.
Notropis proserpinus	Proserpine Shiner	V	U.S.A.
Notropis saladonis		E	Mexico
Notropis semperasper	Roughhead Shiner	R	U.S.A.
Notropis simus	Bluntnose Shiner	E	[Mexico], U.S.A.
Notropis welaka	Bluenose Shiner	R	U.S.A.
Notropis xanthicara	Cuatro Cienegas Shiner	E	Mexico
Oreodaimon quathlambae	Drakensberg Minnow	E	Lesotho
Phenacobius teretulus	Kanawha Minnow	V	U.S.A.
Phoxinus cumberlandensis	Blackside Dace	V	U.S.A.
Plagopterus argentissimus	Woundfin	E	U.S.A.
Pogonichthys ciscoides	Clear Lake Splittail	Ex	[U.S.A.]
Pogonichthys macrolepidotus	Splittail	R	U.S.A.
Probarbus jullieni	Ikan Temoleh	K	South-east Asia
Ptychocheilus lucius	Colorado River Squawfish	E	U.S.A.
Rasbora vaterifloris	Vateria Flower Rasbora	V	Sri Lanka
Relictus solitarius	Relict Dace	V	U.S.A.
Rhinichthys deaconi	Las Vegas Dace	Ex	[U.S.A.]
Rhinichthys osculus (subspecies)	Speckled Dace	T*	Canada, U.S.A.
Semotilis lumbee	Sandhills Chub	R	U.S.A.

Stypodon signifer	Stumptooth Minnow	Ex	[Mexico]
Tanakia tanago	Tokyo Bitterling	E	Japan
Tiaroga cobitus	Loach Minnow	V	U.S.A.
Tylognathus klatti		E	Turkey
Family Cobitidae			
Lepidocephalus jonklassi	Spotted Loach	E	Sri Lanka
Leptobotia curta	Ayumodoki	E	Japan
Family Catostomidae			
Catostomus bernardini	Yaqui Sucker	V	Mexico, U.S.A.
Catostomus fumeiventris	Owens Sucker	R	U.S.A.
Catostomus luxatus	Lost River Sucker	V	U.S.A.
Catostomus microps	Modoc Sucker	E	U.S.A.
Catostomus warnerensis	Warner Sucker	E	U.S.A.
Catostomus wigginsi	Opata Sucker	R	Mexico
Chasmistes brevirostris	Shortnose Sucker	E	U.S.A.
Chasmistes cujus	Cui-ui	E	U.S.A.
Chasmistes liorus	June Sucker	E	U.S.A.
Chasmistes muriei	Snake River Sucker	Ex	[U.S.A.]
Cycleptus elongatus	Blue Sucker	V	U.S.A.
Lagochila lacera	Harelip Sucker	Ex	[U.S.A.]
Moxostoma hamiltoni	Rustyside Sucker	R	U.S.A.
Moxostoma hubbsi	Copper Redhorse	V	Canada
Xyrauchen texanus	Razorback Sucker	E	U.S.A.
Order CHARACIFORMES			
Family Characidae			
Catabasis acuminatus		E	Brazil
Gymnocharacinus bergi	Naked Characin	V	Argentina
Order SILURIFORMES			
Family Diplomystidae			
Diplomystes chilensis	Tollo de Agua Dulce	E	Chile
Family Ictaluridae			
Ictalurus mexicanus	Rio Verde Catfish	R	Mexico
Ictalurus pricei	Yaqui Catfish	R	Mexico
Noturus bailei	Smoky Madtom	E	U.S.A.

Noturus flavipinnis	Yellowfin Madtom	E	U.S.A.
Noturus furiosus	Carolina Madtom	V	U.S.A.
Noturus gilberti	Orangefin Madtom	V	U.S.A.
Noturus lachneri	Ouachita Madtom	E	U.S.A.
Noturus munitus	Frecklebelly Madtom	V	U.S.A.
Noturus placidus	Neosho Madtom	V	U.S.A.
Noturus stanauli	Pygmy Madtom	R	U.S.A.
Noturus taylori	Caddo Madtom	R	U.S.A.
Noturus trautmani	Scioto Madtom	E	U.S.A.
Prietella phreatophila	Muzquiz Blindcat	I	Mexico
Satan eurystomus	Widemouth Blindcat	R	U.S.A.
Trogloglanis pattersoni	Toothless Blindcat	R	U.S.A.
Family Bagridae			
Austroglanis barnardi	Barnard's Rock-catfish	E	South Africa
Austroglanis gilli	Clanwilliam Rock-catfish	R	South Africa
Austroglanis sclateri	Rock-catfish	R	South Africa
Coreobagrus ichikawai	Nekogigi	E	Japan
Gephryoglanis gilli	Clanwilliam Rock-catfish	R	South Africa
Family Pangasiidae			
Pangasianodon gigas	Giant Catfish	V	Mekong Basin
Pangasius sanitwongsei	Pla Thepa	R	Thailand
Family Sisoridae			
Oreoglanis siamensis		I	Thailand
Family Clariidae			
Clarias cavernicola	Cave Catfish	E	Namibia
Family Mochokidae			
Chiloglanis bifurcus	Incomati Rock Catlet	V	South Africa
Order SALMONIFORMES			
Family Umbridae			
Novumbra hubbsi	Olympic Mudminnow	R	U.S.A.
Family Osmeridae			
Osmerus spectrum	Pygmy Smelt	R	Canada, U.S.A.

Family Retropinnidae			
Prototroctes maraena	Australian Grayling	V	Australia, Tasmania
Prototroctes oxyrhynchus	New Zealand Greyling	Ex	[New Zealand]
Family Galaxiidae			
Galaxias fontanus	Swan Galaxias	E	Tasmania
Galaxias johnstoni	Clarence Galaxias	E	Tasmania
Galaxias parvus	Small Pedder Galaxias	V	Tasmania
Galaxias pedderensis	Pedder Galaxias	V	Tasmania
Galaxias postvectis	Shortjawed Kokopu	I	New Zealand
Galaxias tanycephalus	Saddled Galaxias	V	Tasmania
Neochanna burrowsius	Canterbury Mudfish	R	New Zealand
Neochanna diversus	Black Mudfish	I	New Zealand
Family Salmonidae			
Coregonus alpenae	Longjaw Cisco	Ex	[Great Lakes (North America)]
Coregonus artedii	Cisco	R	Great Lakes (North America)
Coregonus canadensis	Atlantic Whitefish	E	Great Lakes (North America)
Coregonus hoyi	Bloater	I	Great Lakes (North America)
Coregonus johannae	Deepwater Cisco	Ex	Great Lakes (North America)
Coregonus kiyi	Kiyi	V	Great Lakes (North America)
Coregonus nigripinnis	Blackfin Cisco	V	Great Lakes (North America)
Coregonus reighardi	Shortnose Cisco	V	Great Lakes (North America)
Coregonus zenithicus	Shortjaw Cisco	V	Great Lakes (North America)
Salmo apache	Apache Trout	V	U.S.A.
Salmo chrysogaster	Mexican Golden Trout	I	Mexico
Salmo clarki (subspecies)	Cutthroat Trout	T*	U.S.A.
Salmo gilae	Gila Trout	E	U.S.A.
Salmo platycephalus	Ala Balik	E	Turkey
Salvelinus agassizi	Silver Trout	Ex	[U.S.A.]
Salvelinus confluentus	Bull Trout	R	Canada, U.S.A.
Stenodus leucichthys leucichthys		V	U.S.S.R.
Order PERCOPSIFORMES			
Family Amblyopsidae			
Amblyopsis rosae	Ozark Cavefish	V	U.S.A.
Amblyopsis spelaea	Northern Cavefish	V	U.S.A.
Speoplatyrhinus poulsoni	Alabama Cavefish	V	U.S.A.

Order CYPRINODONTIFORMES			
Family Aplocheilidae			
Nothobranchius sp.	Caprivi Killifish	E	Namibia
Family Rivulidae			
Cynolebias boitonei	Brasilia Lyrefin	R	Brazil
Cynolebias constanciae		V	Brazil
Cynolebias marmoratus	Ginger Pearlfish	E	Brazil
Cynolebias minimus	Minute Pearlfish	I	Brazil
Cynolebias opalescens	Opalescent Pearlfish	E	Brazil
Cynolebias splendens	Splendid Pearlfish	E	Brazil
Rivulus robustus	Mexican Rivulus	R	Mexico
Family Fundulidae			
Fundulus albolineatus	Whiteline Topminnow	Ex	[U.S.A.]
Fundulus julisia	Barrens Topminnow	V	U.S.A.
Fundulus sciadicus	Plains Topminnow	R	U.S.A.
Fundulus waccamensis	Waccamaw Killifish	V	U.S.A.
Lucania interioris	Sardinilla Cuatro Cienegas	V	Mexico
Family Valenciidae			
Valencia hispanica	Valencia Toothcarp	E	Spain
Family Poeciliidae			
Gambusia alvarezi	Guayacon de San Gregorio	R	Mexico
Gambusia amistadensis	Amistad Gambusia	Ex	[U.S.A.]
Gambusia gaigei	Big Bend Gambusia	E	U.S.A.
Gambusia georgei	San Marcos Gambusia	Ex?	U.S.A.
Gambusia heterochir	Clear Creek Gambusia	E	U.S.A.
Gambusia hurtadoi	Guayacon de Hacienda Dolores	R	Mexico
Gambusia longispinis	Guayacon de Cuatro Cienegas	R	Mexico
Gambusia nobilis	Pecos Gambusia	E	U.S.A.
Micropanchax schoelleri		I	Egypt
Poeciliopsis occidentalis	Gila Topminnow	V	Mexico, U.S.A.
Xiphophorus couchianus	Monterrey Platyfish	E	Mexico
Xiphophorus gordoni	Cuatro Cienegas Platyfish	R	Mexico

Family Goodeidae			
Allotoca maculata	Opal Goodeid	V	Mexico
Ataeniobius toweri	Striped Goodeid	V	Mexico
Characodon audax	Bold Characodon	R	Mexico
Characodon garmani	Parras Characodon	Ex	[Mexico]
Characodon lateralis	Rainbow Goodeid	V	Mexico
Crenichthys baileyi	White River Springfish	V	U.S.A.
Crenichthys nevadae	Railroad Valley Springfish	V	U.S.A.
Empetrichthys latos	Pahrump Killifish	V	U.S.A.
Empetrichthys merriami	Ash Meadows Killifish	Ex	[U.S.A.]
Girardinichthys multivariatus		E	Mexico
Girardinichthys viviparus		E	Mexico
Skiffia francescae	Golden Skiffia	E	Mexico
Xenoophorus captivus	Potosi Goodeid	R	Mexico
Family Cyprinodontidae			
Campellolebias brucei	Santa Catarina Sabrefin	E	Brazil
Cualac tessellatus	Media Luna Killie	E	Mexico
Cyprinodon alvarezi	Potosi Pupfish	E	Mexico
Cyprinodon atrorus	Bolson Pupfish	R	Mexico
Cyprinodon beltrani	Blackfin Pupfish	V	Mexico
Cyprinodon bifasciatus	Cuatro Cienegas Pupfish	R	Mexico
Cyprinodon bovinus	Leon Springs Pupfish	E	U.S.A.
Cyprinodon diabolis	Devils Hole Pupfish	E	U.S.A.
Cyprinodon elegans	Comanche Springs Pupfish	E	U.S.A.
Cyprinodon eximius	Conchos Pupfish	V	Mexico, U.S.A.
Cyprinodon fontinalis	Carbonera Pupfish	E	Mexico
Cyprinodon labiosus	Thicklip Pupfish	V	Mexico
Cyprinodon latifasciatus	Parras Pupfish	Ex	[Mexico]
Cyprinodon macrolepis	Bigscale Pupfish	R	Mexico
Cyprinodon macularius	Desert Pupfish	E	Mexico, U.S.A.
Cyprinodon maya	Maya Pupfish	V	Mexico
Cyprinodon meeki	Mezquital Pupfish	V	Mexico
Cyprinodon nevadensis	Amargosa Pupfish	V	U.S.A.
Cyprinodon pachycephalus	Bighead Pupfish	V	Mexico
Cyprinodon radiosus	Owens Pupfish	E	U.S.A.
Cyprinodon simus	Vertical Jaw Pupfish	V	Mexico
Cyprinodon tularosa	White Sands Pupfish	V	U.S.A.
Cyprinodon verecundus	Largefin Pupfish	V	Mexico

Cyprinodon spp.	Perritos de Sandia	Ex?	Mexico
Kosswigichthys asquamatus	Scaleless Killifish	V	Turkey
Megupsilon aporus	Caterina Pupfish	E	Mexico
Orestias cuvieri		E	Bolivia
Order BELONIFORMES			
Family Adrianichthyidae			
Adrianichthys kruyti		E	Indonesia
Xenopoecilus poptae		E	Indonesia
Xenopoecilus sarasinorum		E	Indonesia
Order ATHERINIFORMES			
Family Atherinidae			
Menidia conchorum	Key Silverside	R	U.S.A.
Menidia extensa	Waccamaw Silverside	V	U.S.A.
Family Melanotaeniidae			
Melanotaenia eachamensis	Lake Eacham Rainbowfish	V	Australia
Pseudomugil mellis	Honey Blue-eye	V	Australia
Family Phallostethidae			
Phallostethus dunckeri		I	Malaysia
Order SYNGNATHIFORMES			
Family Syngnathidae			
Hippocampus capensis	Knysna Seahorse	V	South Africa
Syngnathus watermayeri	River Pipefish	V	South Africa
Order SYNBRANCHIFORMES			
Family Synbranchidae			
Ophisternon candidum	Blind Cave Eel	I	Australia
Order SCORPAENIFORMES			
Family Cottidae			
Cottus asperrimus	Rough Sculpin	R	U.S.A.
Cottus echinatus	Utah Lake Sculpin	Ex	[U.S.A.]
Cottus extensus	Bear Lake Sculpin	R	U.S.A.
Cottus greenei	Shoshone Sculpin	V	U.S.A.
Cottus princeps	Klamath Lake Sculpin	R	U.S.A.
Cottus pygmaeus	Pygmy Sculpin	V	U.S.A.

Order PERCIFORMES			
Family Percichthyidae			
Maccullochella macquariensis	Trout Cod	E	Australia
Maccullochella ikei	Eastern Freshwater Cod	E	Australia
Maccullochella n.sp.	Mary River Cod	I	Australia
Family Centrarchidae			
Ambloplites cavifrons	Roanoke Bass	R	U.S.A.
Micropterus notius	Suwannee Bass	R	U.S.A.
Micropterus treculi	Guadalupe Bass	V	U.S.A.
Family Percidae			
Ammocrypta asprella	Crystal Darter	R	U.S.A.
Ammocrypta pellucida	Eastern Sand Darter	V	Canada, U.S.A.
Etheostoma acuticeps	Sharphead Darter	V	U.S.A.
Etheostoma aquali	Coppercheek Darter	R	U.S.A.
Etheostoma australe	Conchos Darter	V	Mexico
Etheostoma boschungi	Slackwater Darter	V	U.S.A.
Etheostoma cinereum	Ashy Darter	R	U.S.A.
Etheostoma ditrema	Coldwater Darter	V	U.S.A.
Etheostoma fonticola	Fountain Darter	E	U.S.A.
Etheostoma histrio	Harlequin Darter	I	U.S.A.
Etheostoma kanawhae	Kanawha Darter	R	U.S.A.
Etheostoma luteovinctum	Redband Darter	R	U.S.A.
Etheostoma mariae	Pinewoods Darter	R	U.S.A.
Etheostoma microlepidum	Smallscale Darter	R	U.S.A.
Etheostoma moorei	Yellowcheek Darter	R	U.S.A.
Etheostoma nianguae	Niangua Darter	R	U.S.A.
Etheostoma nuchale	Watercress Darter	E	U.S.A.
Etheostoma okaloosae	Okaloosa Darter	V	U.S.A.
Etheostoma pallididorsum	Paleback Darter	R	U.S.A.
Etheostoma pottsi	Mexican Darter	V	Mexico
Etheostoma rubrum	Bayou Darter	V	U.S.A.
Etheostoma saludae	Saluda Darter	R	U.S.A.
Etheostoma sellare	Maryland Darter	E	U.S.A.
Etheostoma striatulum	Striated Darter	V	U.S.A.
Etheostoma trisella	Trispot Darter	V	U.S.A.
Etheostoma tuscumbia	Tuscumbia Darter	V	U.S.A.
Perca schrenki	Balkhash Perch	R	U.S.S.R.

Percina antesella	Amber Darter	V	U.S.A.
Percina aurolineata	Goldline Darter	V	U.S.A.
Percina burtoni	Blotchside Logperch	R	U.S.A.
Percina cymatotaenia	Bluestripe Darter	R	U.S.A.
Percina jenkinsi	Conasauga Logperch	E	U.S.A.
Percina lenticula	Freckled Darter	R	U.S.A.
Percina macrocephala	Longhead Darter	V	U.S.A.
Percina nasuta	Longnose Darter	V	U.S.A.
Percina pantherina	Leopard Darter	V	U.S.A.
Percina rex	Roanoke Logperch	V	U.S.A.
Percina tanasi	Snail Darter	R	U.S.A.
Percina uranidea	Stargazing Darter	R	U.S.A.
Romanichthys valsanicola	Asprete	E	Rumania
Family Sciaenidae			
Totoaba macdonaldi	Totoaba	E	Mexico
Family Cichlidae			
Astatotilapia brevis	Orange-fringed Largemouth	R	South Africa
Cichlasoma bartoni	Mojarra Caracolera	V	Mexico
Cichlasoma labridens	Mojarra	V	Mexico
Cichlasoma minckleyi	Mojarra	V	Mexico
Cichlasoma pantostictum	Mojarra	R	Mexico
Cichlasoma steindachneri	Mojarra	R	Mexico
Konia dikume	Dikume	V	Cameroon
Konia eisentrauti	Konye	V	Cameroon
Mistichthys luzonensis	Sinarapan	V	Philippines
Myaka myaka	Myaka Myaka	V	Cameroon
Pungu maclareni	Pungu	V	Cameroon
Sarotherodon caroli	Fissi	V	Cameroon
Sarotherodon linnellii	Unga	V	Cameroon
Sarotherodon lohbergeri	Leka Keppe	V	Cameroon
Sarotherodon steinbachi	Kululu	V	Cameroon
Serranochromis meridianus	Lowveld Largemouth	R	South Africa
Stomatepia mariae	Nsess	V	Cameroon
Stomatepia mongo	Mongo	V	Cameroon
Stomatepia pindu	Pindu	V	Cameroon
Tilapia guinasana	Otjikoto Tilapia	E	Namibia
haplochromine spp. (c. 250 spp.)	Lake Victoria Cichlids	E	East Africa
tilapiine spp. (2 spp.)	Lake Victoria Cichlids	E	East Africa

Family Mugilidae			
Myxus capensis	Freshwater Mullet	R	South Africa
Family Eleotridae			
Mogurnda n.sp.	Flinders Gudgeon	V	Australia
Hypseleotris dayi	Golden Sleeper	R	South Africa
Family Gobiidae			
Chlamydogobius n.sp.	Elizabeth Springs Goby	V	Australia
Croilia mossambica	Burrowing Goby	I	South Africa
Eucyclogobius newberryi	Tidewater Goby	R	U.S.A.
Lentipes concolor	O'opu Alamo'o	V	U.S.A.
Redigobius dewaali	Checked Goby	R	South Africa
Sicydium stimpsoni	O'opu Nopili	R	U.S.A.
Silhouettea sibayi	Sibayi Goby	R	South Africa
Taenioides jacksoni	Bearded Eelgoby	V	South Africa
Family Anabantidae			
Sandelia bainsii	Eastern Province Rocky	V	South Africa
Family Belontiidae			
Belontia signata	Combtail	R	Sri Lanka
Malpulutta kretseri	Ornate Paradisefish	V	Sri Lanka

INVERTEBRATES
other than Insects

Phylum CILIOPHORA

CLASS POLYHYMENOPHOREA			
Order HETEROTRICHIDA			
Family Stentoridae			
Stentor introversus	Tartar's Stentor	K	U.S.A.

Phylum CNIDARIA

CLASS ANTHOZOA			
Order GORGONACEA			
Family Plexauridae			
Eunicella verrucosa	Broad Sea Fan	K	Mediterranean Sea, North-east Atlantic Ocean
Family Coralliidae			
Corallium	Precious Corals (20 species)	CT	Mediterranean Sea, Pacific Ocean
Order ACTINIARIA			
Family Edwardsiidae			
Nematostella vectensis	Starlet Sea Anemone	V	U.K., North America
Order ANTIPATHARIA			
Family Anthipathidae	Black Coral (*c* 150 species)	CT	Caribbean, Indo-Pacific

Phylum PLATYHELMINTHES

CLASS TURBELLARIA			
Order TRICLADIDA			
Family Kenkiidae			
Kenkia rhynchida	Malheur Cave Planarian	R	U.S.A.
Romankenkius pedderensis	Lake Pedder Planarian	Ex?	[Tasmania]
Sphalloplana holsingeri	Holsinger's Groundwater Planarian	E	U.S.A.
Sphalloplana subtilis	Biggers' Groundwater Planarian	E	U.S.A.

Phylum NEMERTEA

CLASS ENOPLA			
Order HOPLONEMERTEA			
Family Prosorhochmidae	Land Nemertines		
Antiponemertes allisonae		V	New Zealand
Argonemertes australiensis		R	Australia
Argonemertes hillii		R	Australia
Argonemertes stocki		R	Australia
Geonemertes rodericana		R	Rodrigues
Katechonemertes nightingaleensis		R	Tristan da Cunha
Leptonemertes chalicophora		R	Madeira, Azores, Canary Is
Pantinonemertes agricola		R	Bermuda
Pantinonemertes enalios		K	Australia
Pantinonemertes winsori		K	Australia

Phylum MOLLUSCA

CLASS GASTROPODA			
Order ARCHAEOGASTROPODA			
Family Turbinidae			
Turbo marmoratus	Green Snail	CT	Indo-Pacific
Family Neritidae			
Neritilia hawaiiensis		I	Hawaii
Order MESOGASTROPODA			
Family Valvatidae			
Valvata utahensis	Utah Roundmouth Snail	I	U.S.A.
Family Hydrobiidae			
Amnicola deserta	St George Snail	I	U.S.A.
Aphaostracon asthenes	Blue Spring Aphaostracon	I	U.S.A.
Aphaostracon monas	Wekiwa Springs Aphaostracon	I	U.S.A.
Aphaostracon pycnas	Compact Hydrobe Snail	I	U.S.A.
Aphaostracon xynoeiictus	Fenney's Spring Hydrobe Snail	I	U.S.A.
Cincinnatia helicogyra	Helicoid Spring Snail	I	U.S.A.
Cincinnatia mica		I	U.S.A.
Cincinnatia monroensis	Enterprise Spring Snail	I	U.S.A.

Cincinnatia parva		I	U.S.A.
Cincinnatia ponderosa	Ponderous Spring Snail	I	U.S.A.
Cincinnatia vanhyningi	Seminole Spring Snail	I	U.S.A.
Cincinnatia wekiwae	Wekiwa Spring Snail	I	U.S.A.
Coahuilix hubbsi	Coahuilix de Hubbs Snail	V	Mexico
Cochliopa texana	Phantom Cave Snail	I	U.S.A.
Cochliopina milleri	Miller's Snail	V	Mexico
Coxiella striata		I	Tasmania
Durangonella coahuilae	Durangonella de Coahuila Snail	V	Mexico
Fluminicola avernalis	Muddy Valley Turban Snail	I	U.S.A.
Fluminicola erythopoma	Point of Rocks Spring Snail	E	U.S.A.
Fluminicola merriami	Pahranagat Valley Turban Snail	I	U.S.A.
Fluminicola robusta	Elk Island Snail	I	U.S.A.
Fluminicola sp. (3 species)		I	U.S.A.
Fontelicella sp.	Roswell Fontelicella	V	U.S.A.
Fontelicella micrococus		I	U.S.A.
Fontelicella robusta		I	U.S.A.
Fontelicella sp. (2 species)		I	U.S.A.
Fontelicella robusta walkeri		I	U.S.A.
Fonticella neomexicana	Socorro Spring Snail	Ex?	[U.S.A.]
Glacidorbis pedderi		I	Tasmania
Glacidorbis pawpela		I	Tasmania
Lithoglyphus columbiana	Giant Columbia River Spire Snail	E	U.S.A.
Marstonia agarhecta		I	U.S.A.
Marstonia castor		I	U.S.A.
Marstonia ogmoraphe	Obese Marstonia Snail	I	U.S.A.
Marstonia pachyta		I	U.S.A.
Mexipyrgus carranzae	Mexipyrgus de Carranza Snail	V	Mexico
Mexipyrgus churinceanus	Mexipyrgus de Churince Snail	V	Mexico
Mexipyrgus escobedae	Mexipyrgus de Escobeda Snail	V	Mexico
Mexipyrgus lugoi	Mexipyrgus de Lugo Snail	V	Mexico
Mexipyrgus mojarralis	Mexipyrgus de West El Mojarral Snail	V	Mexico
Mexipyrgus multilineatus	Mexipyrgus de East El Mojarral Snail	V	Mexico
Mexithauma quadripaludium	Mexithauma de Cienegas Snail	V	Mexico
Nymphophilus minckleyi	Nymphophilus de Minckley Snail	V	Mexico
Paludiscala caramba	Paludiscala de Oro Snail	V	Mexico
Somatogyrus catanotus		I	U.S.A.
Somatogyrus parvulus		I	U.S.A.
Somatogyrus tenax		I	U.S.A.
Stiobia nana		I	U.S.A.

Tryonia cheatumi	Cheatum's Snail	I	U.S.A.
Tryonia clathrata	White River Snail	I	U.S.A.
Tryonia imitator	California Brackish Water Snail	I	U.S.A.
Tryonia n.sp. (6 species)		I	U.S.A.
Family Assimineidae			
Assiminea infirma	Badwater Snail	I	U.S.A.
Assiminea sp.	Pecos Assiminea Snail	V	U.S.A.
Family Pleuroceridae			
Apella alabamensis		Ex	U.S.A.
Apella babylonia		Ex	U.S.A.
Athearni anthonyi	Anthony's River Snail	Ex	U.S.A.
Athearni crassa	Crass River Snail	I	U.S.A.
Elimia albanyensis		I	U.S.A.
Goniobasis albanyensis	Albany River Snail	I	U.S.A.
Io arwigera arwigera		E	U.S.A.
Io fluvialis	Spiny River Snail	V	U.S.A.
Leptoxis crassa		I	U.S.A.
Leptoxis praerosa	Mainstream River Snail	Ex	U.S.A.
Leptoxis subumbilicata		I	U.S.A.
Lithasia armigera	Armigerous River Snail	I	U.S.A.
Lithasia duttoniana	Dutton's River Snail	I	U.S.A.
Lithasia geniculata	Geniculate River Snail	I	U.S.A.
Lithasia jayana	Jay's River Snail	E	U.S.A.
Lithasia lima	Elk River File Snail	E	U.S.A.
Lithasia salebrosa	Rugged River Snail	E	U.S.A.
Lithasia verrucosa	Verrucose File Snail	I	U.S.A.
Family Strombidae			
Strombus gigas	Queen Conch	CT	Caribbean
Family Cymatiidae			
Charonia tritonis	Triton's Trumpet	R	Indo-Pacific
Order GYMNOSOMATA			
Family Corambidae			
Doridella batava	Zuiderzee Doridella Sea Slug	K	Netherlands

Order BASOMMATOPHORA			
Family Lymnaeidae			
Lymnaea kingii	Utah Band Snail	I	U.S.A.
Myxas glutinosa	Glutinous Snail	V	Europe
Stagnicola pilsbryi	Fish Springs Pond Snail	I	U.S.A.
Family Lancidae			
Fisherola nuttalli	Giant Columbia River Limpet	I	U.S.A.
Family Physidae			
Physa spelunca	Wyoming Cave Snail	I	U.S.A.
Physa utahensis	Utah Bubble Snail	I	U.S.A.
Physa zionis	Zion Canyon Snail	I	U.S.A.
Physa sp.	Snake River Physa Snail	V	U.S.A.
Physa virgata		I	U.S.A.
Stenophysa microstriata	Fish Lake Snail	I	U.S.A.
Family Planorbidae			
Ancylastrum cumingianus	Tasmanian Freshwater 'Limpet'	E	Tasmania
Helisoma jacksonense	Jackson Lake Snail	I	U.S.A.
Helisoma magnificum	Cape Fear Ramshorn Snail	I	U.S.A.
Segmentina nitida		V	Europe
Taphius eucosmius eucosmius	Greenfield Ramshorn Snail	I	U.S.A.
Order STYLOMMATOPHORA			
Family Achatinellidae			
Achatinella (41 species)	22 species Little Agate Shells	Ex	[Hawaii]
	19 species Little Agate Shells	E	Hawaii
Partulina confusa		E	Hawaii
Partulina crassa		Ex	[Hawaii]
Partulina fusoidea		V	Hawaii
Partulina montagui		Ex	[Hawaii]
Partulina perdix		V	Hawaii
Partulina splendida		V	Hawaii
Perdicella kuhnsi		E/V	Hawaii
Family Partulidae			
Partula aurantia		Ex	Moorea)
Partula exigua		Ex	Moorea)

Partula gibba		E	Guam
Partula hebe		E	Society Is
Partula mirabilis		Ex	Moorea
Partula mooreana		Ex	Moorea
Partula radiolata		K	Guam
Partula salifana		K	Guam
Partula suturalis		Ex	Moorea
Partula taeniata		Ex	Moorea
Partula tohiveana		Ex	Moorea
Samoana abbreviata	Short Samoan Tree Snail	I	American Samoa
Samoana diaphana		E	Society Is
Samoana solitaria		E	Society Is
Family Amastridae			
Carelia (all species)		Ex	[Hawaii]
Thaanumia sp.		Ex?	[Hawaii]
Family Pupillidae			
Leiostyla abbreviata		V	Madeira
Leiostyla cassida		V	Madeira
Leiostyla corneocostata		V	Madeira
Leiostyla gibba		V	Madeira
Leiostyla lamellosa		V	Madeira
Sterkia clementina	San Clemente Island Blunt-top Snail	I	U.S.A.
Family Vertiginidae			
Vertigo alabamensis		I	U.S.A.
Vertigo angustior		V	Europe
Vertigo genesii		V	Europe
Vertigo geyeri		V	Europe
Vertigo hebardi		I	U.S.A.
Vertigo moulinsiana		V	Europe
Family Clausiliidae			
Balea perversa		V	Europe
Family Succineidae			
Catinella arenaria		V	Europe
Oxyloma haydeni kanabensis	Kanab Amber Snail	I	U.S.A.
Oxyloma sarsi		V	Europe

Family Streptaxidae			
Gulella plantii	Plant's Gulella Snail	V	South Africa
Family Rhytididae			
Paryphanta busbyi	Kauri Amber Snail	V	New Zealand
Paryphanta compta		V	New Zealand
Paryphanta fletcheri		V	New Zealand
Paryphanta gilliesi		V	New Zealand
Paryphanta hochstetteri		V	New Zealand
Paryphanta lignaria		V	New Zealand
Paryphanta rossiana		V	New Zealand
Paryphanta traversi		V	New Zealand
Family Acavidae			
Anoglypta launcestonensis	Granulated Tasmanian Snail	E	Tasmania
Family Bulimulidae			
Bulimulus (31 endemic species)		E	Galapagos Is
Placostylus ambagiosus		V	New Zealand
Placostylus bollonsi		V	New Zealand
Placostylus hongii	Flax Snail	V	New Zealand
Family Arionidae			
Binneya notabilis	Slug Snail	V	U.S.A.
Geomalacus maculosus	Kerry Slug	R	Ireland
Family Endodontidae			
Anguispira picta	Painted Snake-coiled Forest Snail	V	U.S.A.
Discus defloratus		V	Madeira
Discus guerinianus		V	Madeira
Discus macclintocki	Iowa Pleistocene Snail	E	U.S.A.
Discus marmorensis		I	U.S.A.
Thaumatodon hystricelloides		E	Western Samoa
Family Helicodiscidae			
Helicodiscus diadema		I	U.S.A.
Helicodiscus hexodon		I	U.S.A.
Polygyriscus virginianus		E	U.S.A.

Family Helicarionidae			
Diastole matafaoi	Mount Matafao Different Snail	I	American Samoa
Family Zonitidae			
Glyphyalinia pecki		I	U.S.A.
Paravitrea clappi		I	U.S.A.
Family Polygyridae			
Ashmunella pasonis		I	U.S.A.
Mesodon archeri	Archer's Toothed Land Snail	I	U.S.A.
Mesodon clarki nantahala	Noonday Snail	V	U.S.A.
Mesodon clausus trossulus		I	U.S.A.
Mesodon clenchi	Clench's Middle-toothed Land Snail	I	U.S.A.
Mesodon jonesianus		I	U.S.A.
Mesodon magazinensis	Magazine Mountain Middle-toothed Snail	I	U.S.A.
Polygyra hippocrepis		I	U.S.A.
Polygyra peregrina	Strange Many-whorled Land Snail	I	U.S.A.
Polygyriscus virginianus	Virginia Fringed Mountain Snail	E	U.S.A.
Stenotrema hubrichti		I	U.S.A.
Stenotrema leai cheatumi		I	U.S.A.
Stenotrema pilsbryi	Pilsbry's Narrow-apertured Land Snail	I	U.S.A.
Triodopsis mullani magnidentata		I	U.S.A.
Triodopsis occidentalis	Western Three-toothed Land Snail	I	U.S.A.
Triodopsis platysayoides	Flat-spired Three-toothed Snail	E	U.S.A.
Vespericola karokorum	Karok Indian Snail	V	U.S.A.
Family Ammonitellidae			
Ammonitella yatesi	Yate's Snail	I	U.S.A.
Family Camaenidae			
Papustyla pulcherrima	Manus Green Tree Snail	R	Papua New Guinea
Family Oreohelicidae			
Oreohelix avaloensis		I	U.S.A.
Oreohelix idahoensis idahoensis	Idaho Banded Mountain Snail	V	U.S.A.
Oreohelix jugalis intersum		R	U.S.A.
Oreohelix jugalis jugalis		V	U.S.A.
Oreohelix jugalis vortex	Vortex Banded Mountain Snail	R	U.S.A.
Oreohelix peripherica weberiana	Coalville Mountain Snail	I	U.S.A.

Oreohelix strigosa goniogyra	Carinated Striate Banded Mountain Snail	R	U.S.A.
Oreohelix vortex		R	U.S.A.
Oreohelix waltoni	Walton's Banded Mountain Snail	I	U.S.A.
Family Helminthoglyptidae			
Helminthoglypta allynsmithi	Allyn Smith's Banded Snail	I	U.S.A.
Helminthoglypta arrosa mattolensis		I	U.S.A.
Helminthoglypta arrosa miwoka		I	U.S.A.
Helminthoglypta arrosa pomoensis		I	U.S.A.
Helminthoglypta arrosa williamsi		I	U.S.A.
Helminthoglypta callistoderma		I	U.S.A.
Helminthoglypta mohaveana		I	U.S.A.
Helminthoglypta nickliniana awania	Nicklin's Peninsula Snail	I	U.S.A.
Helminthoglypta nickliniana bridgesi		I	U.S.A.
Helminthoglypta nickliniana contracosta		I	U.S.A.
Helminthoglypta sequoicola consors		I	U.S.A.
Helminthoglypta traski coelata		I	U.S.A.
Helminthoglypta walkeriana	Banded Dune Snail	V	U.S.A.
Micrarionta facta	Concentrated Snail	V	U.S.A.
Micrarionta feralis	Fraternal Snail	I	U.S.A.
Micrarionta gabbi	Gabb's Snail	I	U.S.A.
Micrarionta immaculata		I	U.S.A.
Micrarionta indiaensis cathedralis		I	U.S.A.
Micrarionta intercisa		I	U.S.A.
Micrarionta morongoana	Colorado Desert Snail	I	U.S.A.
Micrarionta opuntia	Prickly Pear Snail	I	U.S.A.
Micrarionta redimita		I	U.S.A.
Micrarionta rowelli bakerensis		I	U.S.A.
Micrarionta rowelli mccoiana	California McCoy Snail	I	U.S.A.
Monadenia circumcarinata		I	U.S.A.
Monadenia fidelis minor		I	U.S.A.
Monadenia fidelis pronotis	Rocky Coast Snail	I	U.S.A.
Monadenia hillebrandi yosemitansis	Indian Yosemite Snail	I	U.S.A.
Monadenia hirsutis		I	U.S.A.
Monadenia monbritoni		I	U.S.A.
Monadenia mormonum buttoni		I	U.S.A.
Monadenia mormonum hirsuta		I	U.S.A.
Monadenia selosci		I	U.S.A.
Monadenia setosa	Trinity Bristle Snail	E	U.S.A.

Monadenis troglodytes		I	U.S.A.
Sonorella eremita		I	U.S.A.
Sonorella metcalfi		I	U.S.A.
Family Helicidae			
Caseolus calculus		V	Madeira
Caseolus commixta		V	Madeira
Caseolus sphaerula		V	Madeira
Discula leacockiana		V	Madeira
Discula tabellata		V	Madeira
Discula testudinalis		V	Madeira
Discula turricula	Cima Discula	V	Madeira
Geomitra moniziana		V	Madeira
Helix pomatia	Roman Snail	R	Europe
Helix subplicata		V	Madeira
Helix tryoni		I	U.S.A.
Family Elonidae			
Elona quimperiana	Escargot de Quimper	R	France, Spain
CLASS BIVALVIA			
Succinea chittenangoensis	Chittenango Ovate Amber Snail	V	U.S.A.
Orthalicus reses	Stock Island Snail	V	U.S.A.
Order PTERIOIDA			
Family Pteriidae			
Pinctada margaritifera	Black-lipped Pearl Oyster	CT	Indo-Pacific
Pinctada maxima	Gold-lipped Pearl Oyster	CT	Indo-Pacific
Order UNIONOIDA			
Family Unionidae			
Alasmidonta arcula		I	U.S.A.
Alasmidonta atropurpurea		I	U.S.A.
Alasmidonta heterodon	Dwarf Wedge Mussel	E	U.S.A.
Alasmidonta raveneliana		E	U.S.A.
Alasmidonta robusta		E	U.S.A.
Alasmidonta wrightiana		I	U.S.A.
Arkansia wheeleri	Wheeler's Pearly Mussel	E	U.S.A.

Canthyria collina	James River Spiny Mussel	V	U.S.A.
Canthyria spinosa		I	U.S.A.
Carunculina pulla	Savannah Shore Mussel	R	U.S.A.
Conradilla caelata	Birdwing Pearly Mussel Birdwing	E	U.S.A.
Cyprogenia aberti	Western Fan-shell Pearly Mussel	E	U.S.A.
Cyprogenia irrorata	Eastern Fan-shell Pearly Mussel	I	U.S.A.
Cyrtonaias tampicoensis tecomatensis	Tampico Pearly Mussel	E	Mexico
Dromus dromas	Dromedary Pearly Mussel	E	U.S.A.
Elliptio marsupiobesa	Cape Fear Spike Pearly Mussel	I	U.S.A.
Elliptio nigella	Recovery Pearly Mussel	Ex	[U.S.A.]
Elliptio spinosa	Georgia Spiny Mussel	R	U.S.A.
Elliptio steinstansana	Tar River Spiny Mussel	E	U.S.A.
Elliptio waccamawensis	Waccamaw Spike	R	U.S.A.
Elliptio sp.	Waccamaw Lake Pearly Mussel	I	U.S.A.
Epioblasma arcaeformis	Arc-form Pearly Mussel	Ex?	[U.S.A.]
Epioblasma biemarginata		Ex	[U.S.A.]
Epioblasma brevidens		E	U.S.A.
Epioblasma capsaeformis		E	U.S.A.
Epioblasma curtisi		I	U.S.A.
Epioblasma flexuosa	Arcuate Pearly Mussel	Ex	[U.S.A.]
Epioblasma florentina curtisi	Curtis Pearly Mussel	Ex?	[U.S.A.]
Epioblasma florentina florentina	Yellow-blossom Pearly Mussel	E	U.S.A.
Epioblasma haysiana	Acorn Pearly Mussel	E	U.S.A.
Epioblasma lefevrei	Lefevre's Pearly Mussel	Ex	[U.S.A.]
Epioblasma lenior	Stone's Pearly Mussel	Ex	[U.S.A.]
Epioblasma lewisi	Lewis Pearly Mussel	Ex?	[U.S.A.]
Epioblasma metastriata		E	U.S.A.
Epioblasma othcaloogensis	Southern Acorn Riffle Shell	E	U.S.A.
Epioblasma penita	Penitent Mussel	E	U.S.A.
Epioblasma personata	Fine-rayed Pearly Mussel	Ex	[U.S.A.]
Epioblasma propinqua	Nearby Pearly Mussel	Ex	[U.S.A.]
Epioblasma sampsoni	Sampson's Pearly Mussel	E	U.S.A.
Epioblasma stewardsoni	Steward's Pearly Mussel	Ex	[U.S.A.]
Epioblasma sulcata delicata	White Cat's Paw Mussel	E	U.S.A.
Epioblasma sulcata sulcata	Purple Cat's Paw Mussel	E	U.S.A.
Epioblasma torulosa gubernaculum	Green-blossom Pearly Mussel	E	U.S.A.
Epioblasma torulosa rangiana	Tan-blossom Pearly Mussel	E	Canada, U.S.A.
Epioblasma torulosa torulosa	Tubercled-blossom Pearly Mussel	E	U.S.A.
Epioblasma triquetra	Snuffbox	V	U.S.A.

Epioblasma turgidula	Turgid-blossom Pearly Mussel	E	U.S.A.
Epioblasma walkeri	Tan Riffle Shell Mussel	E	U.S.A.
Fusconaia collina	Virginia Spiny Mussel	I	U.S.A.
Fusconaia cuneolus	Fine-rayed Pigtoe Pearly Mussel	E	U.S.A.
Fusconaia edgariana	Shiny Pigtoe Pearly Mussel	E	U.S.A
Hemistena lata	Cracking Pearly Mussel	E	U.S.A.
Lampsilis dolabraeformis		Ex?	[U.S.A.[
Lampsilis fasciola		Ex	[U.S.A.]
Lampsilis higginsi	Higgin's Eye Pearly Mussel	E	U.S.A.
Lampsilis hostonia		Ex	[U.S.A.]
Lampsilis orbiculata	Pink Mucket Pearly Mussel	E	U.S.A.
Lampsilis perovalis		I	U.S.A.
Lampsilis rafinesqueana	Neosho Pearly Mussel	E	U.S.A.
Lampsilis streckeri		I	U.S.A.
Lampsilis virescens	Alabama Lamp Pearly Mussel	E	U.S.A.
Lasmigona holstonia		I	U.S.A.
Leptodea leptodon	Scale Shell	I	U.S.A.
Lexingtoni dolabelloides	Slab-side Pearly Mussel	I	U.S.A.
Megalonaias nicklineana	Nicklin's Pearly Mussel	E	Mexico
Obovaria retusa	Golf Stick Pearly Mussel	I	U.S.A.
Pegias fabula	Little Winged Pearly Mussel	E	U.S.A.
Plectomeris dombeyana		Ex	[U.S.A.]
Plethobasus cicatricosus	White Warty Back Pearly Mussel	E	U.S.A.
Plethobasus cooperianus	Cumberland Pigtoe	E	U.S.A.
Pleurobema clava	Northern Club Shell	I	U.S.A.
Pleurobema curtum	Curtus' Mussel	E	U.S.A.
Pleurobema marshalli	Marshall's Mussel	E	U.S.A.
Pleurobema oviforme		I	U.S.A.
Pleurobema plenum	Rough Pigtoe Pearly Mussel	E	U.S.A.
Pleurobema rubrum		I	U.S.A.
Pleurobema taitianum	Judge Tait's Mussel	E	U.S.A.
Potamilus capax	Fat Pocketbook	E	U.S.A.
Potamilus inflatus		I	U.S.A.
Quadrula cylindrica strigillata	Rough Rabbit's Foot Pearly Mussel	I	U.S.A.
Quadrula fragosa	Rough Maple Leaf Pearly Mussel	Ex	U.S.A.
Quadrula intermedia	Cumberland Monkeyface Pearly Mussel	E	U.S.A.
Quadrula sparsa	Appalachian Monkey Face Pearly Mussel	E	U.S.A.
Quadrula stapes	Stirrup Shell	E	U.S.A.
Simponaia ambigua		I	U.S.A.
Simpsoniconcha ambigua	Salamander Mussel	I	U.S.A.

Toxolasma cylindrella	Pale Lilliput Pearly Mussel	E	U.S.A.
Villosa choctawensis	Choctaw Pearly Mussel	I	U.S.A.
Villosa fabalis		I	U.S.A.
Villosa ortmanni	Ortmann's Pearly Mussel	R	U.S.A.
Villosa perpurea	Fine-rayed Purple Pearly Mussel	I	U.S.A.
Villosa trabalis	Cumberland Bean Pearly Mussel	E	U.S.A.
Family Margaritiferidae			
Cumberlandia monodonta	Spectacle Case Pearly Mussel	I	U.S.A.
Margaritifera auricularia	Spengler's Freshwater Mussel	I	Europe
Margaritifera margaritifera	Freshwater Pearl Mussel	V	Europe, North America
Margaritifera marrianae	Alabama Pearl Shell	I	U.S.A.
Order VENEROIDA			
Family Tridacnidae			
Hippopus hippopus	Horse's Hoof Clam	I	Indo-Pacific
Hippopus porcellanus	China Clam	I	Indo-Pacific
Tridacna crocea	Crocus Clam	K	Indo-Pacific
Tridacna derasa	Southern Giant Clam	V	Indo-Pacific
Tridacna gigas	Giant Clam	V	Indo-Pacific
Tridacna maxima	Small Giant Clam	K	Indo-Pacific
Tridacna squamosa	Scaly Clam	I	Indo-Pacific
Family Sphaeriidae			
Pisidium ultramontanum		I	U.S.A.
Family Hyriidae			
Velesunio moretonicus		I	Tasmania
Family Caryodidae			
Anoglypta launcestonensis		I	Tasmania

Phylum ANNELIDA

Taxon	Common name	Status	Distribution
CLASS POLYCHAETA			
Order EUNICIDA			
Family Eunicidae			
Eunice viridis	Palolo Worm	K	Pacific
CLASS HIRUDINOIDEA			
Order ARHYNCHOBDELLAE			
Family Hirudinidae			
Hirudo medicinalis	Medicinal Leech	I	Europe
CLASS OLIGOCHAETA			
Order HAPLOTAXIDA			
Family Megascolecidae			
Megascolides americanus	Washington Giant Earthworm	E	U.S.A.
Megascolides australis	Giant Gippsland Earthworm	V	Australia
Megascolides macelfreshi	Oregon Giant Earthworm	E	U.S.A.
Family Acanthodrilidae	South African Acanthodriline Earthworms		
Chilota (13 species)		V	South Africa
Diplotrema (16 species)		V	South Africa
Microscolex (9 species)		V	South Africa
Udeina (59 species)		V	South Africa
Family Microchaetidae			
Microchaetus (33 species)	South African Giant Earthworms	V	South Africa
Tritogenia (5 species)		V	South Africa
Family Lutodrilidae			
Lutodrilus multivesiculatus		R	U.S.A.
Family Komarekionidae			
Komarekiona eatoni		V	U.S.A.

Phylum ARTHROPODA
Subphylum CHELICERATA

Species	Common name	Category	Distribution
CLASS MEROSTOMATA			
Order XIPHOSURA			
Family Limulidae			
Carcinoscorpius rotundicauda	Horseshoe Crabs	K	Coastal waters - Japan to Indonesia
Limulus polyphemus		K	Atlantic coast of North America
Tachypleus gigas		K	Coastal waters - Japan to Indonesia
Tachypleus tridentatus		K	Coastal waters - Japan to Indonesia
CLASS ARACHNIDA			
Order ARANEAE			
Family Theraphosidae			
Brachypelma smithi	Red-kneed Tarantula	K	Mexico
Family Dipluridae			
Macrothele calpeiana		V	Spain
Macrothele cretica		I	Crete
Family Ctenizidae			
Cyclocosimia torreya		I	U.S.A.
Family Telemidae			
Telema (whole genus)		I	U.S.A.
Family Eresidae			
Eresus niger	Ladybird Spider	I	Europe
Family Linyphiidae			
Troglophantes gracilis	Kocevje Subterranean Spider	R	Yugoslavia
Troglophantes similis	Kocevje Subterranean Spider	R	Yugoslavia
Troglophantes spinipes	Kocevje Subterranean Spider	R	Yugoslavia
Family Asauridae			
Dolomedes plantarius	Great Raft Spider	V	Northern Europe
Family Araneidae			
Meta dolloff		I	U.S.A.

Family Gnaphosidae			
Cesonia irvingi		I	Bahamas, U.S.A.
Family Lycosidae			
Adelocosa anops	No-eyed Big-eyed Wolf Spider	E	U.S.A.
Lycosa ericeticola		I	U.S.A.
Pardosa diuturna	Glacier Bay Wolf Spider	R	U.S.A.
Sosippus placidus		I	U.S.A.
Order PSEUDOSCORPIONIDA			
Family Neobisiidae			
Microcreagris imperialis		I	U.S.A.
Order OPILIONES			
Family Phalangodidae			
Banksula melones	Melones Bay Harvestman	V	U.S.A.

Subphylum CRUSTACEA

CLASS CRUSTACEA			
Order ANOSTRACA			
Family Artemiidae			
Artemia monica	Mono Lake Brine Shrimp	I	U.S.A.
Family Branchinectidae			
Branchinecta gigas	Giant Fairy Shrimp	I	Western North America
Branchinecta paludosa		R	Czechoslovakia
Order THORACICA			
Family Balanidae			
Armatobalanus nefrens		I	U.S.A.
Balanus aquila		I	U.S.A.
Order ANASPIDACEA			
Family Anaspidae			
Allanaspides helonomus		V	Tasmania
Allanaspides hickmani		V	Tasmania
Anaspides spinulae		V	Tasmania

Species	Common name	Status	Distribution
Anaspides tasmaniae		V	Tasmania
Paranaspides lacustris		V	Tasmania
Family Koonungidae			
Koonunga cursor		R	Tasmania, Australia
Micraspides calmani		R	Tasmania
Family Psammaspididae			
Eucrenonaspides oinotheke		V	Tasmania
Order ISOPODA			
Family Cirolanidae			
Antrolana lira	Madison Cave Isopod	V	U.S.A.
Arubolana imula		I	Netherlands
Mexilana saluposi		K	Mexico
Speocirolana affinis		K	Mexico
Speocirolana interstitialis		K	Mexico
Speocirolana thermydromis		K	Mexico
Family Sphaeromatidae			
Thermosphaeroma dugesi		K	Mexico
Thermosphaeroma milleri		K	Mexico
Thermosphaeroma smithi		K	Mexico
Thermosphaeroma subequalum		K	Mexico
Thermosphaeroma thermophilum	Socorro Isopod	E	U.S.A.
Family Trichoniscidae			
Metatrichoniscoides celticus		V	U.K.
Family Styloniscidae			
Styloniscus sp.		I	Tasmania
Family Scyphacidae			
(*Haloniscus searlei*)		I	Tasmania
Family Armadillidae			
Echinodillo cavaticus		I	Tasmania

Family Phreatoicidae			
Mesacanthotelson setosis		I	Tasmania
Onchotelson brevicaudatus		I	Tasmania
Onchotelson spatulatus		I	Tasmania
Uramphisopus pearsoni		I	Tasmania
Family Asellidae			
Caecidotea barri	Clifton Cave Isopod	I	U.S.A.
Caecidotea macropoda	Bat Cave Isopod	I	U.S.A.
Caecidotea nickajackensis	Nickajack Cave Isopod	I	U.S.A.
Lirceus culveri	Rye Cove Cave Isopod	I	U.S.A.
Lirceus usdagalun	Lee County Cave Isopod	I	U.S.A.
Family Stenasellidae			
Mexistenasellus coahuila		I	Mexico
Mexistenasellus parzefalli	Parzefall's Stenasellid	R	Mexico
Mexistenasellus wilkensi	Wilkens' Stenasellid	R	Mexico
Order AMPHIPODA			
Family Gammaridae			
Gammarus acherondytes	Illinois Cave Amphipod	I	U.S.A.
Gammarus bousfieldi	Bousfield's Amphipod	I	U.S.A.
Gammarus desperatus	Noel's Amphipod	I	U.S.A.
Gammarus hyalieioides	Diminutive Amphipod	I	U.S.A.
Gammarus pecos	Pecos Amphipod	I	U.S.A.
Family Crangonyctidae			
Allocrangonyx hubrichti	Central Missouri Cave Amphipod	I	U.S.A.
Allocrangonyx pellucidus	Oklahoma Cave Amphipod	I	U.S.A.
Crangonyx dearolfi	Pennsylvania Cave Amphipod	I	U.S.A.
Crangonyx grandimanus	Florida Cave Amphipod	I	U.S.A.
Crangonyx hobbsi	Hobb's Cave Amphipod	I	U.S.A.
Stygobromus araeus	Tidewater Interstitial Amphipod	I	U.S.A.
Stygobromus arizonensis	Arizona Cave Amphipod	I	U.S.A.
Stygobromus balconius	Balcones Cave Amphipod	I	U.S.A.
Stygobromus barri	Barr's Cave Amphipod	I	U.S.A.
Stygobromus bifurcatus	Bifurcated Cave Amphipod	I	U.S.A.
Stygobromus bowmani	Bowman's Cave Amphipod	I	U.S.A.
Stygobromus clantoni	Clanton's Cave Amphipod	I	U.S.A.
Stygobromus conradi	Burnsville Cove Cave Amphipod	I	U.S.A.

Stygobromus cooperi	Cooper's Cave Amphipod	I	U.S.A.
Stygobromus dejectus	Cascade Cave Amphipod	I	U.S.A.
Stygobromus elatus	Elevated Spring Amphipod	I	U.S.A.
Stygobromus emarginatus	Greenbrier Cave Amphipod	I	U.S.A.
Stygobromus ephemerus	Ephemeral Cave Amphipod	I	U.S.A.
Stygobromus flagellatus	Ezell's Cave Amphipod	I	U.S.A.
Stygobromus gradyi	Grady's Cave Amphipod	I	U.S.A.
Stygobromus hadenoecus	Devil's Sinkhole Amphipod	I	U.S.A.
Stygobromus harai	Hara's Cave Amphipod	I	U.S.A.
Stygobromus hayi	Hay's Spring Amphipod	I	U.S.A.
Stygobromus heteropodus	Pickle Springs Amphipod	I	U.S.A.
Stygobromus hubbsi	Malheur Cave Amphipod	I	U.S.A.
Stygobromus identatus	Tidewater Stygonectid Amphipod	I	U.S.A.
Stygobromus longipes	Long-legged Cave Amphipod	I	U.S.A.
Stygobromus lucifugus	Rubious Cave Amphipod	Ex	[U.S.A.]
Stygobromus mackenziei	Mackenzie's Cave Amphipod	I	U.S.A.
Stygobromus montanus	Mountain Cave Amphipod	I	U.S.A.
Stygobromus morrisoni	Morrison's Cave Amphipod	I	U.S.A.
Stygobromus mundus	Bath County Cave Amphipod	I	U.S.A.
Stygobromus nortoni	Norton's Cave Amphipod	I	U.S.A.
Stygobromus onondagaensis	Onondaga Cave Amphipod	I	U.S.A.
Stygobromus ozarkensis	Ozark Cave Amphipod	I	U.S.A.
Stygobromus parvus	Minute Cave Amphipod	I	U.S.A.
Stygobromus pecki	Peck's Cave Amphipod	I	U.S.A.
Stygobromus pizzinii	Pizzini's Amphipod	I	U.S.A.
Stygobromus putealis	Wisconsin Well Amphipod	I	U.S.A.
Stygobromus reddelli	Reddell's Cave Amphipod	I	U.S.A.
Stygobromus smithii	Alabama Well Amphipod	I	U.S.A.
Stygobromus spinatus	Spring Cave Amphipod	I	U.S.A.
Stygobromus stellmacki	Stellmack's Cave Amphipod	I	U.S.A.
Stygobromus subtilis	Subtle Cave Amphipod	I	U.S.A.
Stygobromus wengerorum	Wengeror's Cave Amphipod	I	U.S.A.
Family Orchestiidae			
Spelaeorchestia koloana	Kaui Cave Amphipod	I	Hawaii

Order DECAPODA			
Family Atyidae			
Palaemonias alabamae	Alabama Cave Shrimp	I	U.S.A.
Syncaris pacifica	California Freshwater Shrimp	E	U.S.A.
Typhlatya monae	Mona Cave Shrimp	I	Puerto Rico
Family Palaemonidae			
Palaemonetes antrorum	Texas Cave Shrimp	I	U.S.A.
Palaemonetes cummingi	Florida Cave Shrimp	V	U.S.A.
Family Nephropidae			
Homarus americanus	American Lobster	CT	North Atlantic
Homarus gammarus	European Lobster	CT	North-east Atlantic
Nephrops norvegicus	Norway Lobster	CT	North-east Atlantic
Family Cambaridae			
Cambarus batchi		I	U.S.A.
Cambarus bouchardi	Big South Fork Crayfish	I	U.S.A.
Cambarus catagius	Greensboro Burrowing Crayfish	I	U.S.A.
Cambarus chasmodactylus	New River Riffle Crayfish	I	U.S.A.
Cambarus extraneus	Chickamanga Crayfish	I	U.S.A.
Cambarus obeyensis	Obey Crayfish	I	U.S.A.
Cambarus zophonastes		E	U.S.A.
Orconectes jeffersoni	Louisville Crayfish	I	U.S.A.
Orconectes shoupi	Nashville Crayfish	E	U.S.A.
Procambarus acherontis	Orlando Cave Crayfish	I	U.S.A.
Procambarus connus		I	U.S.A.
Procambarus lepiclocdactylus	Pee Dee Lotic Crayfish	I	U.S.A.
Family Astacidae			
Astacus astacus	Noble Crayfish	V	Europe
Austropotamobius pallipes	White-clawed Crayfish	R	Europe
Austropotamobius torrentium		K	Europe
Pacifastacus fortis	Shasta Crayfish	V	U.S.A.
Pacifastacus nigrescens		Ex?	[U.S.A.]
Family Parastacidae			
Astacoides madagascariensis	Madagascar Freshwater Crayfish	I	Madagascar

Astacopsis gouldi	Giant Freshwater Crayfish	V	Tasmania
Astacopsis franklinii		I	Tasmania
Cherax crassimanus		R	West Australia
Engaewa subcoerulea		R	West Australia
Family Palinuridae			
Jasus edwardsii	Rock Lobster	CT	New Zealand
Panulirus argus		CT	Caribbean
Panulirus guttatus	Spotted Spiny Lobster	CT	Caribbean
Panulirus penicillatus		CT	Indo-Pacific
Family Coenobitidae			
Birgus latro	Coconut Crab	R	Indo-Pacific
Family Hippidae			
Emerita emeritus	Sand Crab	K	India, Thailand
Family Pinnotheridae			
Parapinnixa affinis	California Bay Pea Crab	K	U.S.A.

INSECTS

Subphylum UNIRAMIA

CLASS INSECTA

Order THYSANURA			
Family Machilidae			
Machiloides heteropus	Hawaiian Long-palp Bristletail	I	Hawaii
Machiloides perkinsi	Perkin's Club-palp Bristletail	I	Hawaii
Order COLLEMBOLA			
Family Neanuridae			
Acanthanura dendyi		I	Tasmania
Acanthanura n.sp. "mesibovi"		I	Tasmania
Megalanura tasmaniae		I	Tasmania
Womersleymeria bicornis		I	Tasmania
Womersleymeria n.sp. "iresoni"		I	Tasmania
Womersleymeria n.sp. "zachariae"		I	Tasmania
Order EPHEMEROPTERA			
Family Siphlonuridae			
Acanthometropus pecatonica	Pecatonica River Mayfly	Ex	[U.S.A.]
Ameletus falsus	False Mayfly	I	U.S.A.
Isonychia diversa	Diverse Mayfly	I	U.S.A.
Tasmanophlebia lacus-coerulei	Large Blue Lake Mayfly	R	Australia
Family Baetidae			
Heterocleon berneri	Berner's Two-winged Mayfly	I	U.S.A.
Family Oligoneuridae			
Homoeoneuria cahabensis	Cahaba Sand-filtering Mayfly	I	U.S.A.
Homoeoneuria dolani	Blackwater Sand-filtering Mayfly	I	U.S.A.
Family Heptageniidae			
Pseudirion meridionalis	Meridion Blackwater Mayfly	I	U.S.A.
Family Behningiidae			
Dolania americana	American Sand-burrowing Mayfly	I	U.S.A.

Family Ephemeridae			
Ephemera compar	Colorado Burrowing Mayfly	I	U.S.A.
Ephemera triplex	West Virginia Burrowing Mayfly	I	U.S.A.
Pantagenia robusta	Robust Burrowing Mayfly	Ex	[U.S.A.]
Family Ephemerellidae			
Ceratella frisoni	Frison's Mayfly	I	U.S.A.
Ceratella spiculosa	Spicluose Mayfly	I	U.S.A.
Ephemerella argo	Argo Mayfly	I	U.S.A.
Family Caenidae			
Brachycercus flavus	Yellow Mayfly	I	U.S.A.
Order ODONATA			
Family Synlestidae			
Ecchlorolestes nylepytha		E	South Africa
Ecchlorolestes peringueyi		E	South Africa
Phylolestes ethelae		V	Dominican Republic
Family Lestidae			
Austrolestes minjerriba		E	Australia
Family Hemiphlebiidae			
Hemiphlebia mirabilis	Small Damselfly	E	Australia
Family Megapodagrionidae			
Amanipodagrion gilliesi		E	Tanzania
Family Protoneuridae			
Noeneura aaroni		R	Guatemala, U.S.A.
Nososticta pilbara		E	Australia
Family Platycnemididae			
Metacnemis angusta		I	South Africa
Platycnemis mauricana		E	Mauritius
Family Coenagrionidae			
Aciagrion rarum		I	Angola
Agriocnemis solitaria		E	Mauritius

Species	Common name	Status	Distribution
Agriocnemis umbargae		I	Cameroon
Argiagrion leoninium		I	Sierra Leone
Ceriagrion mourae		I	Mozambique
Coenagrion brisbanense		V	Australia
Coenagrion hylas freyi	Frey's Damselfly	E	Austria, Germany, Switzerland
Coenagrion mercuriale	Southern Damselfly	V	Europe
Enallagma camerunense		I	Tropical Africa
Enallagma polychromaticum		I	South Africa
Enallagma recurvatum	Barrens Bluet Damselfly	V	U.S.A.
Ischnura gemina	San Francisco Forktail Damselfly	E	U.S.A.
Megalagrion adytum	Adytum Damselfly	I	Hawaii
Megalagrion amaurodytum fallax	Fallax Damselfly	I	Hawaii
Megalagrion amaurodytum peles	Pele Damselfly	I	Hawaii
Megalagrion amaurodytum waianaenum	Waianae Damselfly	I	Hawaii
Megalagrion jugorum	Jugorum Damselfly	Ex?	[Hawaii]
Megalagrion leptodemus	Leptodemas Damselfly	I	Hawaii
Megalagrion molokaiense	Molokai Damselfly	I	Hawaii
Megalagrion nesiotes	Nesiotes Damselfly	Ex?	[Hawaii]
Megalagrion nigrohamatum	Nigrohamatum Damselfly	I	Hawaii
Megalagrion nigrolineatum	Blackline Damselfly	I	Hawaii
Megalagrion oahuensis	Oahu Damselfly	I	Hawaii
Megalagrion oceanicum	Oceanic Damselfly	I	Hawaii
Megalagrion pacificum	Pacific Damselfly	E	Hawaii
Megalagrion xanthomelas	Orange-black Damselfly	I	Hawaii
Mortonagrion hirosei		E	Japan
Pseudagrion quadrioculatum		K	Zaire
Teinobasis alluaudi alluaudi		E	Seychelles
Family Pseudostigmatidae			
Mecistogaster asticta		V	Brazil
Mecistogaster pronoti		V	Brazil
Family Calopterygidae			
Calopteryx angustipennis		I	U.S.A.
Calopteryx syriaca		E	Turkey, Syria, Jordan
Family Epiophlebiidae			
Epiophlebia laidlawi	Relict Himalayan Dragonfly	V	India, Nepal

Species	Common name	Status	Distribution
Family Gomphidae			
Antipodogomphus hodgkini		E	Australia
Cornigomphus guineensis		I	Tropical Africa
Erpetogomphus lampropeltis		K	U.S.A.
Gomphus carolinus	Sandhills Clubtail Dragonfly	K	U.S.A.
Gomphus consanguis	Cherokee Clubtail Dragonfly	R	U.S.A.
Gomphus diminutus	Diminutive Clubtail	R	U.S.A.
Gomphus geminatus	Twin-striped Clubtail	R	U.S.A.
Gomphus graslini		R	France, Spain
Gomphus hodgesi	Hodge's Clubtail	R	U.S.A.
Gomphus maxwelli		R	U.S.A.
Gomphus modestus	Gulf Clubtail	R	U.S.A.
Gomphus ozakensis		R	U.S.A.
Gomphus parvidens		R	U.S.A.
Gomphus sandrius	Tennessee Clubtail Dragonfly	I	U.S.A.
Gomphus septima	Septima's Clubtail Dragonfly	R	U.S.A.
Gomphus townesi	Bronze Clubtail Dragonfly	I	U.S.A.
Ictinogomphus dobsoni		E	Australia
Isomma hieroglyphicum		I	Madagascar
Onychogomphus assimilis		R	Turkey, U.S.S.R.
Onychogomphus macrodon		E	Jordan, Israel, Turkey
Ophiogomphus acuminatus		R	U.S.A.
Ophiogomphus anomalus		V	Eastern North America
Ophiogomphus cecilia	Grüne Keiljungter	E	Europe to Siberia
Ophiogomphus edmundo	Edmund's Snaketail Dragonfly	Ex?	[U.S.A.]
Ophiogomphus howei	Howe's Midget Snaketail Dragonfly	V	U.S.A.
Ophiogomphus incurvatus		R	U.S.A.
Ophiogomphus i. alleghaniensis	Alleghany Snaketail Dragonfly	I	U.S.A.
Paragomphus sinaiticus		R	Egypt, Niger
Progomphus bellei	Belle's Sand Variegated Clubtail	R	U.S.A.
Stylurus flavipes	Gomphus à Pattes Jeunes	I	North Palearctic
Stylurus potulentus	Yellow-sided Clubtail	V	U.S.A.
Stylurus townesi		R	U.S.A.
Family Neopetaliidae			
Archipetalia auricuata		I	Tasmania
Family Petaluridae			
Petalura pulcherrima		V	Australia

Family Aeshnidae			
Acanthaeshna victoria		V	Australia
Aeshna meruensis		R	Tanzania
Aeshna persephone		R	U.S.A.
Aeshna viridis	L'Aeschne Verte	I	Europe to Siberia
Anax georgius		I	Tropical Africa
Austroaeschna hardyi		I	Tasmania
Brachytron pratense	(Spring Hawker)	I	Belgium, Germany, U.K.
Indophlebia asiatica		V	India
Family Cordulegastridae			
Cordulegaster mzymtae		E	Turkey, U.S.S.R.
Cordulegaster sayi	Florida Spiketail Dragonfly	E	U.S.A.
Family Corduliidae			
Antipodochlora braueri		I	New Zealand
Austrocordulia territoria		E	Australia
Libellulosoma minuta		I	Madagascar
Macromia margarita		R	U.S.A.
Macromia splendens	Shining Macromia Dragonfly	R	France, Portugal, Spain
Macromia wabashensis	Wabash Belted Skimmer Dragonfly	K	U.S.A.
Neurocordulia clara	Apalachicola Twilight Skimmer Dragonfly	I	U.S.A.
Oxygastra curtisii	Orange-spotted Emerald	V	North Africa, West Europe
Somatochlora brevicincta		R	Canada
Somatochlora calverti	Calverts' Emerald	R	U.S.A.
Somatochlora hineana	Ohio Emerald Dragonfly	E	U.S.A.
Somatochlora incurvata		R	Eastern North America
Somatochlora margarita	Big Thicket Emerald Dragonfly	R	U.S.A.
Somatochlora ozarkensis		R	U.S.A.
Synthemis macrostigma orientalis		I	Tasmania
Synthemiopsis gomphomacromioides		I	Tasmania
Williamsonia lintneri	Banded Bog Skimmer Dragonfly	V	U.S.A.
Family Libellulidae			
Aethiothemis wataliki		K	Congo
Allorhizucha campioni		K	Sierra Leone
Anectothemis apicalis		K	Tropical Africa
Brachythemis fuscopalliata		E	Iraq, Israel, Turkey
Brachythemis liberiensis		I	Guinea Bissau

Congothemis longistyla		K	Zaire
Eleuthemis beuttikofera quadrigutta		K	Mozambique, Zimbabwe
Leucorrhinia albifrons	Leucorrhine à Front Blanc	I	Europe, West Siberia
Leucorrhinia caudalis	Leucorrhine à Large Queue	I	Europe, West Siberia
Libellula angelina		E	Japan
Libellula jerseana	Purple Chaser	K	U.S.A.
Monardithemis flava		V	Angola, Zambia
Orthetrum rubens		I	Tropical Africa
Palpopleura albifrons		I	Gabon
Sympetrum dilatatum		Ex?	[St Helena]
Trithemis hartwigi		I	Eq. Guinea
Trithemis nigra		I	Sao Tome
Urothemis thomasi		K	Eastern Arabia
Order BLATTARIA			
Family Blattidae			
Aspiduchus cavernicola	Tuna Cave Roach	I	Puerto Rico
Order MANTODEA			
Family Mantidae			
Apteromantis aptera		E	Spain
Order GRYLLOBLATTARIA			
Family Grylloblattidae			
Grylloblatta chirurgica	Mount St Helens' Grylloblattid	V	U.S.A.
Order ORTHOPTERA			
Family Stenopelmatidae			
Ammopelmatus kelsoensis	Kelso Jerusalem Cricket	I	U.S.A.
Ammopelmatus muwu	Port Conception Jerusalem Cricket	I	U.S.A.
Deinacrida carinata	Herekopare Island Weta	V	New Zealand
Deinacrida fallai	Poor Knights Weta	V	New Zealand
Deinacrida heteracantha	Wetapunga	V	New Zealand
Deinacrida rugosa	Stephens Island Weta	V	New Zealand
Deinacrida tibiospina		I	New Zealand
Stenopelmatus cahuilaensis	Coachella Valley Jerusalem Cricket	I	U.S.A.
Stenopelmatus navajo	Navajo Jerusalem Cricket	I	U.S.A.
Family Rhaphidophoridae			
Daihinibaenetes arizonensis	Arizona Giant Sand Treader Cricket	I	U.S.A.

Macrobaenetes kelsoensis	Kelso Giant Sand Treader Cricket	I	U.S.A.
Macrobaenetes valgum	Coachelia Giant Sand Treader Cricket	I	U.S.A.
Pristoceuthophilus sp.	Samwell Cave Cricket	I	U.S.A.
Tasmanoplectron isolatum		I	Tasmania
Utabaenetes tanneri	Tanner's Black Camel Cricket	I	U.S.A.
Family Tettigoniidae			
Baetica ustulata		V	Spain
Banza nihoae	Nihoa Banza Conehead Katydid	I	Hawaii
Belocephalus micanopy	Big Pine Key Conehead Katydid	I	U.S.A.
Belocephalus sleighti	Keys Short-winged Conehead Katydid	I	U.S.A.
Conocephaloides remotus	Remote Conehead Katydid	I	Hawaii
Idiostatus middlekaufi	Middlekauf's Shieldback Katydid	I	U.S.A.
Neduba extincta	Antioch Dunes Shieldback Katydid	Ex	[U.S.A.]
Neduba longipennis	Santa Monica Shieldback Katydid	I	U.S.A.
Saga pedo	Predatory Bush Cricket	V	Southern Europe
Family Gryllotalpidae			
Gryllotalpa major	Prairie Mole Cricket	I	U.S.A.
Family Gryllidae			
Caconemobius howarthi	Howarth's Cave Cricket	I	Hawaii
Caconemobius schauinslandi	Schauinsland's Bush Cricket	I	Hawaii
Caconemobius varius	Kaumana Cave Cricket	I	Hawaii
Cycloptilum irregularis	Keys Scaly Cricket	I	U.S.A.
Leptogryllus deceptor	Oahu Deceptor Bush Cricket	I	Hawaii
Oecanthus laricis	Laricis Tree Cricket	I	U.S.A.
Thaumatogryllus cavicola	Volcanoes Cave Cricket	I	Hawaii
Thaumatogryllus variegatus	Kauai Thin-footed Bush Cricket	I	Hawaii
Family Eumastacidae			
Eumorsea pinaleno	Pinaleno Monkey Grasshopper	I	U.S.A.
Psychomastix deserticola	Desert Monkey Grasshopper	I	U.S.A.
Family Acrididae			
Acrolophitus pulchellus	Idaho Point-headed Grasshopper	I	U.S.A.
Appalachia arcena	Michigan Bog Grasshopper	I	U.S.A.
Calliptamus baiulus		I	Tasmania
Chloaeltis aspasma	Siskiyou Chloealtis Grasshopper	I	U.S.A.
Spharagemon superbum		I	U.S.A.

Family Tetrigidae			
Tetrix sierrana	Sierra Pygmy Grasshopper	I	U.S.A.
Tettigidea empedonepia	Torreya Pygmy Grasshopper	I	U.S.A.
Order PHASMATOPTERA			
Family Phasmatidae			
Dryococelus australis	Lord Howe Island Stick-insect	Ex	[Lord Howe I.]
Order DERMAPTERA			
Family Labiduridae			
Labidura herculeana	St Helena Earwig	E	St Helena
Order PLECOPTERA			
Family Nemouridae			
Lednia tumana	Meltwater Stonefly	I	U.S.A.
Nemours wahkeena	Wahkeena Falls Flightless Stonefly	I	U.S.A.
Family Notonemouridae			
Kimminsoperla biloba		I	Tasmania
Kimminsoperla williamsi		I	Tasmania
Family Capniidae			
Capnia lacustra	Lake Tahoe Benthic Stonefly	I	U.S.A.
Family Leuctridae			
Leuctra szczytkoi	Schoolhouse Springs Stonefly	I	U.S.A.
Family Taeniopterygidae			
Taeniopteryx starki	Leon River Stonefly	I	U.S.A.
Family Perlidae			
Beloneuria jamesae	Cheaha Stonefly	I	U.S.A.
Beloneuria georgiana	Georgia Stonefly	I	U.S.A.
Hansonoperla appalachia	Hanson's Appalachian Stonefly	I	U.S.A.
Family Chloroperlidae			
Alloperla roberti	Robert's Stonefly	Ex	[U.S.A.]
Family Peltoperlidae			
Soliperla fenderi	Fender's Stonefly	I	U.S.A.

Family Eustheniidae			
Eusthenia nothofagi	Otway Stonefly	E	Australia
Eusthania reticulata		I	Tasmania
Family Gripopterygidae			
Leptoperla cacuminis	Mount Kosciusko Wingless Stonefly	R	Australia
Riekoperla darlingtoni	Mount Donna Buang Wingless Stonefly	R	Australia
Order ZORAPTERA			
Family Zorotypidae			
Zorotypus swezeyi	Swezey's Zoroapteran	I	Hawaii
Order ANOPLURA			
Family Haematopinidae			
Haematopinus oliveri	Pygmy Hog Sucking Louse	E	India
Order HEMIPTERA			
Family Reduviidae			
Empicoris pulchrus	Pulchrus Thread Bug	I	Hawaii
Siacella smithi	Smith's Reduviid Bug	I	Hawaii
Nesidiolestes ana	Ana Wingless Thread Bug	I	Hawaii
Nesidiolestes insularis	Mount Tantalus Wingless Thread Bug	I	Hawaii
Nesidiolestes roberti	Robert's Wingless Thread Bug	I	Hawaii
Nesidiolestes selium	Selium Wingless Thread Bug	I	Hawaii
Family Miridae			
Cyrtopeltis phyllostegiae	Phyllostegian Leaf Bug	I	Hawaii
Kalania hawaiiensis	Lanai Leaf Bug	I	Hawaii
Kalania sp.	Oshu Leaf Bug	I	Hawaii
Family Lygaeidae			
Metrarga obscura	Mauna Loa Seed Bug	I	Hawaii
Neseis alternatus	Kauai Band-legged Seed Bug	I	Hawaii
Neseis haleakalae	Mount Haleakala Seed Bug	I	Hawaii
Nesocryptias villosa	Villosan Flightless Seed Bug	I	Hawaii
Nysius frigatensis	French Frigate Shoal Seed Bug	I	Hawaii
Nysius neckerensis	Necker Goosefoot Seed Bug	I	Hawaii
Nysius nihoae	Nihoae Seed Bug	I	Hawaii
Nysius sulfusus	Necker Bunchgrass Seed Bug	I	Hawaii

Oceanaides bryani	Bryan's Seed Bug	I	Hawaii
Oceanides perkensi	Perkin's Seed Bug	I	Hawaii
Oceanides rugosiceps	Rough-headed Seed Bug	I	Hawaii
Family Rhopalidae			
Ithamar annectans	Annectans Bug	I	Hawaii
Ithamar hawaiiense	Hawaiian bug	I	Hawaii
Family Mesoveliidae			
Cavaticovelia aaa	Aaa Water Treader Bug	I	U.S.A.
Family Macroveliidae			
Oravelia pege	Dry Creek Cliff Strider Bug	I	U.S.A.
Family Naucoridae			
Ambrysus amargosus	Ash Meadows Bug	E	U.S.A.
Pelocoris shoshone	Amargosa Bug	I	U.S.A.
Family Belostomatidae			
Belostoma saratogae	Saratoga Springs Bug	I	U.S.A.
Order HOMOPTERA			
Family Cixiidae			
Oliarus consimilis	Kauai Particoloured Planthopper	I	Hawaii
Oliarus discrepans	Wild Cotton Planthopper	I	Hawaii
Oliarus lanaiensis	Lanai Planthopper	I	Hawaii
Oliarus lihue	Lihue Planthopper	I	Hawaii
Oliarus myoporicola	Barber's Point Planthopper	I	Hawaii
Family Delphacidae			
Nesorestias filicicola	Mt Tantalus Shortwing Fern Planthopper	I	Hawaii
Nesosydne acuta	Iao Valley Planthopper	I	Hawaii
Nesosydne bridwelli	Bridewell's Planthopper	I	Hawaii
Nesosydne cyrtandrae	Nahiku Planthopper	I	Hawaii
Nesosydne cyrtandricola	Glenwood Planthopper	I	Hawaii
Nesosydne kuschei	Kusche's Planthopper	I	Hawaii
Nesosydne leahi	Diamond Head Planthopper	I	Hawaii
Nesosydne longipes	Long-footed Planthopper	I	Hawaii
Nesosydne sulcata	Keanae Planthopper	I	Hawaii

Family Cicadidae			
Magicicada cassini	Cassini Periodical Cicada	V	U.S.A.
Magicicada septendecim	Decim Periodical Cicada	V	Canada
Magicicada septendecula	Decula Periodical Cicada	V	U.S.A.
Family Tettigarctidae			
Tettigarcta tormentosa		I	Tasmania
Family Cicadellidae			
Felexamia rubranura	Red-veined Prairie Leafhopper	I	U.S.A.
Family Aphididae			
Ceriferella leucopogonis		I	Tasmania
Family Pseudococcidae			
Clavicoccus erinaceus		Ex	[Hawaii]
Phyllococcus oahuensis		Ex	[Hawaii]
Order NEUROPTERA			
Family Ithonidae			
Oliarces clara		I	Hawaii, U.S.A.
Family Mantispidae			
Mantispa styriaca		K	South & Central Europe
Family Hemerobiidae			
Nesothauma halakalae	Haleakala Spongillafly	I	Hawaii
Pseudopsectra cookeorum	Cooke's Spongillafly	I	Hawaii
Pseudopsectra lobipennis	Lobe-wing Spongillafly	I	Hawaii
Pseudopsectra swezeyi	Swezey's Spongillafly	I	Hawaii
Pseudopsectra usingeri	Usinger's Spongillafly	I	Hawaii
Family Ascalaphidae			
Libelloides libelluloides		K	Europe
Libelloides macaronius		K	Europe
Family Myrmeleontidae			
Acanthaclisis occitanica		K	Europe
Dendroleon pantherinus		K	Europe

Distoleon tetragrammicus		K	Europe
Eidoleon perjurus	Molokai Antlion	I	Hawaii
Myrmeleon formicarius		K	Europe
Order COLEOPTERA			
Family Carabidae			
Agonum belleri	Beller's Ground Beetle	I	U.S.A.
Aplothorax burchelli		E	St Helena
Calosoma sycophanta	Puppenrauber	V	Europe, North Africa, U.S.S.R.
Carabus intricatus	Blue Ground Beetle	V	Europe
Carabus olympiae		E	Italy
Elaphrus viridis	Delta Green Ground Beetle	V	U.S.A.
Mormolyce phyllodes	Ghost Walker Beetle	V	Malaysia
Sphaeroderus schaumi shenandoah	Schaum's Blue Ridge Ground Beetle	I	U.S.A.
Family Cicindelidae			
Cicindela arenicola	Idaho Dunes Tiger Beetle	I	U.S.A.
Cicindela cazieri	Cazier's Tiger Beetle	I	U.S.A.
Cicindela chlorocephala smythi	Smyth's Tiger Beetle	I	U.S.A.
Cicindela columbica	Columbia River Tiger Beetle	E	U.S.A.
Cicindela dorsalis dorsalis	North-eastern Beach Tiger Beetle	I	U.S.A.
Cicindela latesignata obliviosa	Oblivious Tiger Beetle	I	U.S.A.
Cicindela limbata albissima	Coral Pink Dunes Tiger Beetle	I	U.S.A.
Cicindela marginata	Tiger Beetle	I	U.S.A.
Cicindela marginipennis	Cobblestone Tiger Beetle	I	U.S.A.
Cicindela nevadica olmosa	Los Olmos Tiger Beetle	I	U.S.A.
Cicindela nigrocoerula subtropica	Subtropical Blue-black Tiger Beetle	I	U.S.A.
Cicindela obsoleta neojuvenalis	Neojuvenile Tiger Beetle	I	U.S.A.
Cicindela puritana	Puritan Tiger Beetle	I	U.S.A.
Cicindela tranquebarica viridissima	Greenest Tiger Beetle	I	U.S.A.
Family Haliplidae			
Brychius hungerfordi	Hungerford's Crawling Water Beetle	I	U.S.A.
Haliplus nitens	Disjunct Crawling Water Beetle	I	U.S.A.
Family Dytiscidae			
Agabus rumppi	Death Valley Diving Beetle	I	U.S.A.
Desmopachria conchramis	Fig Seed Diving Beetle	I	U.S.A.
Dytiscus latissimus		E	North & Central Europe, Siberia

Graphoderus bilineatus		E	Central & West Europe
Haideoporus texanus	Texas Cave Beetle	I	U.S.A.
Hydroporus elusivus	Elusive Diving Beetle	I	U.S.A.
Hydroporus folkertsi	Folkert's Diving Beetle	I	U.S.A.
Hydroporus hirsutus	Woolly Diving Beetle	I	U.S.A.
Hydroporus leechi	Leech's Skyline Diving Beetle	I	U.S.A.
Hydroporus simplex	Simple Diving Beetle	I	U.S.A.
Hydroporus spangleri	Spangler's Diving Beetle	I	U.S.A.
Hydroporus sulphurius	Sulphur Springs Diving Beetle	I	U.S.A.
Hydroporus utahensis	Utah Diving Beetle	I	U.S.A.
Hygrotus artus	Mono Lake Diving Beetle	Ex?	[U.S.A.]
Hygrotus curvipes	Curved-foot Diving Beetle	I	U.S.A.
Hygrotus diversipes	Narrow-foot Diving Beetle	I	U.S.A.
Hygrotus fontinalis	Travertine Band-thigh Diving Beetle	I	U.S.A.
Hygrotus sylvanus	Sylvan Diving Beetle	I	U.S.A.
Family Gyrinidae			
Spanglerogyrus albiventris	Red Hills Unique Whirligig Beetle	I	U.S.A.
Family Hydraenidae			
Gymnocthebius maureenae	Maureen's Minute Moss Beetle	I	U.S.A.
Hydraena maureenae	Maureen's Moss Beetle	I	U.S.A.
Limnebius aridus	Animas Minute Moss Beetle	I	U.S.A.
Limnebius texanus	Texas Minute Moss Beetle	I	U.S.A.
Limnebius utahensis	Utah Minute Moss Beetle	I	U.S.A.
Ochthebius crassalus	Wing-shoulder Minute Moss Beetle	I	U.S.A.
Ochthebius putnamensis	Indiana Minute Moss Beetle	I	U.S.A.
Ochthebius reticulatus	Wilbur Springs Minute Moss Beetle	I	U.S.A.
Family Leiodidae			
Glacicavicola bathysciodes	Blind Cave Beetle	I	U.S.A.
Family Silphidae			
Nicrophorus americanus	American Burying Beetle	E	Eastern North America
Family Hydrophilidae			
Chaetarthria leechi	Leech's Water Scavenger Beetle	I	U.S.A.
Chaetarthria utahensis	Utah Water Scavenger Beetle	I	U.S.A.
Cymbiodyta arizonica	Arizona Water Scavenger Beetle	I	U.S.A.

Hydrochara rickseckeri	Ricksecker's Water Scavenger Beetle	I	U.S.A.
Paracymus seclusus	Seclusive Water Scavenger Beetle	I	U.S.A.
Family Lucanidae			
Apterocychus honoluluensis	Kauai Flightless Stag Beetle	E	Hawaii
Dorcus auriculatus		V	New Zealand
Dorcus ithaginis		V	New Zealand
Family Trogidae			
Trox howelli	Caracara Commensal Scarab Beetle	V	U.S.A.
Family Geotrupidae			
Typhaeus hiostius		V	Sardinia
Family Scarabaeidae			
Aegialia concinna	Ciervo Scarab Beetle	I	U.S.A.
Aegialia crescenta	Cresent Dune Scarab Beetle	I	U.S.A.
Aegialia haroyi	Hardy's Scarab Beetle	I	U.S.A.
Aegialia magnifica	Large Scarab Beetle	I	U.S.A.
Anomala exigua	Exiguous Scarab Beetle	I	U.S.A.
Anomala eximia	Archbold Scarab Beetle	I	U.S.A.
Anomala tibialis	Tibial Scarab Beetle	I	U.S.A.
Aphodius fordi	Ford's Beetle	I	U.S.A.
Aphodius troglodytes	Tortoise Commensal Scarab Beetle	I	U.S.A.
Ataenius superficialis	Big Pine Key Dung Beetle	V	U.S.A.
Ataenius woodruffi	Woodruff's Dung Beetle	E	U.S.A.
Copris gopheri	Tortoise Commensal Scarab Beetle	I	U.S.A.
Cyclocephala miamiensis	Miami Roundhead Scarab Beetle	I	U.S.A.
Dynastes hercules	Hercules Beetle	V	Caribbean & Northern South America
Dynastes hercules glaseri	Hercules Beetle	K	Trinidad & Tobago
Dynastes hercules hercules	Hercules Beetle	V	Dominica, Guadeloupe
Dynastes hercules reidi	Hercules Beetle	V	Martinique, St Lucia
Glaresis arenata	Kelso Dune Scarab Beetle	I	U.S.A.
Gronocarus multispinosus	Spiny Florida Sandhill Scarab Beetle	I	U.S.A.
Lichnanthe albopilosa	White Sand Bear Scarab Beetle	I	U.S.A.
Lichnanthe ursina	Pacific Sand Bear Scarab Beetle	I	U.S.A.
Mycotrupes pedester	Scrub Island Burrowing Scarab Beetle	I	U.S.A.
Onthophagus furacatus		V	Austria
Onthophagus polyphemi	Tortoise Commensal Scarab Beetle	I	U.S.A.
Oryctes chevrolati		K	Reunion

Osmoderma eremita	Hermit Beetle	E	Europe
Peltotrupes youngi	Ocala Burrowing Scarab Beetle	I	U.S.A.
Polylamina pubescens	Woody Gulf Dune Scarab Beetle	I	U.S.A.
Polyphylla anteronivea	Saline Valley Snow-front Scarab	I	U.S.A.
Polyphylla avittata	Spotted Warner Valley Dunes Scarab	I	U.S.A.
Polyphylla barbata	Barbate Scarab Beetle	I	U.S.A.
Polyphylla nubila	Atascodera Scarab Beetle	I	U.S.A.
Prodontria lewisi	Cromwell Chafer	V	New Zealand
Pseudocotalpa giulianii	Giuliani's Dune Scarab Beetle	I	U.S.A.
Serica frosti	Frost's Spring Scarab Beetle	I	U.S.A.
Serica tantula	Tantula Scarab Beetle	I	U.S.A.
Trigonopelastes floridana	Scrub Palmetto Flower Scarab Beetle	R/I	U.S.A.
Family Buprestidae			
Buprestis splendens	Goldstreifiger	E	Europe
Family Elmidae			
Atractelmis wawona	Wawawona Riffle Beetle	I	U.S.A.
Cylloepus parkeri	Parker's Riffle Beetle	I	U.S.A.
Dubiraphia brunnescens	Brownish Riffle Beetle	I	U.S.A.
Dubiraphia giulianii	Giuliani's Riffle Beetle	I	U.S.A.
Dubiraphia parva	Little Riffle Beetle	I	U.S.A.
Dubiraphia robusta	Robust Riffle Beetle	I	U.S.A.
Heterelmis stephani	Stephan's Riffle Beetle	I	U.S.A.
Huleechius marroni carolus	Marron's San Carlos Riffle Beetle	I	U.S.A.
Microcylloepus browni	Brown's Riffle Beetle	I	U.S.A.
Optioservus browni	Brown's Riffle Beetle	I	U.S.A.
Optioservus canus	Pinnacles Riffle Beetle	I	U.S.A.
Optioservus phaeus	Scott Riffle Beetle	I	U.S.A.
Stenelmis calida calida	Devil's Hole Warm Spring Riffle Beetle	I	U.S.A.
Stenelmis calida moapa	Moapa Warm Springs Riffle Beetle	I	U.S.A.
Stenelmis douglasensis	Douglas Riffle Beetle	I	U.S.A.
Stenelmis gammoni	Gammon's Riffle Beetle	I	U.S.A.
Zaitzeva thermae	Warm Spring Riffle Beetle	I	U.S.A.
Family Psephenidae			
Acneus beeri	Beer's False Water Penny Beetle	I	U.S.A.
Acneus burnelli	Burnell's False Water Penny Beetle	I	U.S.A.
Alabamaubria starki	Stark's False Water Penny Beetle	I	U.S.A.

Dicranopselaphus variegatus	Variegated False Water Penny Beetle	I	U.S.A.
Psephenus arizonensis	Arizona Water Penny Beetle	I	U.S.A.
Psephenus montanus	White Mountains Water Penny Beetle	I	U.S.A.
Family Elateridae			
Amychus candezei		V	Chatham Is, New Zealand
Amychus granulatus		V	New Zealand
Eanus hatchi	Hatch's Click Beetle	I	Canada, U.S.A.
Eopenthes (17 species)	Hawaiian Click Beetles	E	Hawaii
Itodacnus (whole genus)	Necker Click Beetles	I	Hawaii
Family Eucnemidae			
Paleoxenus dohmi	Dohrn's Elegant Eucnemid Beetle	I	U.S.A.
Family Lampyridae			
Micronaspis floridana	Florida Intertidal Firefly	I	U.S.A.
Photuris brunnipennis floridana	Everglades Browing Firefly	I	U.S.A.
Family Anobiidae			
Holcobius pikoensis	Piko Anobiid Beetle	I	Hawaii
Family Cucujidae			
Cucujus cinnaberinus	Scharlachkäfer	E	Northern & Central Europe
Family Tenebrionidae			
Coelus globosus	Globose Dune Beetle	I	Mexico, U.S.A.
Coelus gracilis	San Joaquin Dune Beetle	I	U.S.A.
Polposipus herculeanus	Frigate Island Giant Tenebrionid Beetle	R	Seychelles
Family Meloidae			
Lytta hoppingi	Hopping's Blister Beetle	I	U.S.A.
Lytta inseperata	Mojave Desert Blister Beetle	I	U.S.A.
Lytta mirifica	Anthony Blister Beetle	I	Mexico, U.S.A.
Lytta moesta	Moestan Blister Beetle	I	U.S.A.
Lytta molesta	Molestan Blister Beetle	I	U.S.A.
Lytta morrisoni	Morrison's Blister Beetle	I	U.S.A.

Family Anthicidae			
Anthicus antiochensis	Antioch Dunes Beetle	I	U.S.A.
Anthicus sacramento	Sacramento Beetle	I	U.S.A.
Family Cerambycidae			
Aeschrithmysus dubautianus		E	Hawaii
Aeschrithmysus swezeyi		E	Hawaii
Aeschrithmysus terryi		E	Hawaii
Cerambyx cerdo	Cerambyx Longicorn	E	Central & Northern Europe
Crossidius mojavensis mojavensis	Mojave Rabbitbrush Longhorn Beetle	E	U.S.A.
Desmocerus californicus dimorphus	Valley Elderberry Longhorn Beetle	V	U.S.A.
Dryobius sexnotatus	Six-banded Longhorn Beetle	I	U.S.A.
Macrodontia cervicornis		K	Brazil, Peru
Morimus funereus		E	Central Europe, U.S.S.R.
Necydalis rudei	Rude's Longhorn Beetle	I	Hawaii
Nesithmysus bridwelli		E	Hawaii
Nesithmysus frobesi		E	Hawaii
Nesithmysus haasi		E	Hawaii
Nesithmysus swezeyi		E	Hawaii
Plagithmysus (49 species)		E	Hawaii
Rosalia alpina	Rosalia Longicorn	E	Central & Northern Europe
Xylotoles costatus		Ex	[Chatham Is]
Family Chrysomelidae			
Donacia idola	Bog Idol Leaf Beetle	I	U.S.A.
Family Aglycyderidae			
Proterhinus (72 species)	Hawaiian Proterhinus Beetles	E	Hawaii
Family Curculionidae			
Anagotus fairburni	Flax Weevil	V	New Zealand
Anagotus turbotti	Turbott's Weevil	V	New Zealand
Deinocossonus nesiotes	Oahu Nesiotes Weevil	E	Hawaii
Dryophthorus distinguendus		Ex	[Hawaii]
Dryotribus mimeticus		Ex	[Hawaii]
Dysticheus rotundicollis	Antioch Dune Weevil	I	U.S.A.

Gymnopholus lichenifer	Lichen Weevil	V	Papua New Guinea
Hadramphus spinipennis		V	Chatham Is
Hadramphus stilbocarpae		V	New Zealand
Hadramphus tuberculatus		V	New Zealand
Heteramphus filicum		E	Hawaii
Heterexis seticostatus		V	New Zealand
Lyperobius huttoni	Speargrass Weevil	V	New Zealand
Macrancylus linearis		Ex	[Hawaii]
Megacolabus sculpturatus		V	New Zealand
Microcryptorhynchus orientissimus		R	Henderson I.
Miloderes nelsoni	Nelson's Weevil	I	U.S.A.
Miloderes rulieni	Rulien's Weevil	I	U.S.A.
Nesotocus giffordi	Gifford's Weevil	I	Hawaii
Nesotocus kauaiensis	Kauai Weevil	I	Hawaii
Nesotocus munroi	Munro's Weevil	I	Hawaii
Nothaldonis peaci		E	New Zealand
Oclandius laeviusculus		V	New Zealand
Oedemasylus laysanensis		Ex	[Hawaii]
Onchobarus langei	Lange's El Segundo Dune Weevil	I	U.S.A.
Oodemas (whole genus)	Windward Chain Weevils	I	Hawaii
Pentarthrum blackburni	Blackburn's Weevil	Ex?	[Hawaii]
Pentarthrum obscura	Obscure Weevil	I	Hawaii
Pentarthrum pritchardias		E	Hawaii
Rhyncogonus hendersoni		R	Henderson I.
Rhyncogonus (22 species)	Hawaiian Snout Beetles	E	Hawaii
Stenotrupis pritchardiae	Nihoa Weevil	I	Hawaii
Trigonoscuta brunnotesselata	Brown-tassel Weevil	I	U.S.A.
Trigonoscuta dorothea dorothea	Dorothy's El Segundo Dune Weevil	I	U.S.A.
Trigonoscuta doyeni	Doyen's Dune Weevil	E/V	U.S.A.
Trigonoscuta rossi	Fort Ross Weevil	Ex?	[U.S.A.]
Trigonoscuta yorbalindae	Yorba Linda Weevil	Ex?	[U.S.A.]
Unas piceus		V	New Zealand
Order MECOPTERA			
Family Apteropanorpidae			
Apteropanorpa tasmanica		I	Tasmania

Species	Common name	Status	Range
Order DIPTERA			
Family Psychodidae			
Nemapalpus nearcticus	Sugarfoot Moth Fly	I	U.S.A.
Family Mycetophilidae			
Arachnocampa tasmaniensis		I	Tasmania
Family Blephariceridae			
Edwardsina gigantea	Giant Torrent Midge	E	Australia
Edwardsina tasmaniensis	Tasmanian Torrent Midge	E	Australia
Family Tabanidae			
Apatalestea rossi	Ross's Apatalestes Tabanid Fly	I	U.S.A.
Asaphomyia floridensis	Florida Asaphomyian Tabanid Fly	I	U.S.A.
Asaphomyia texanus	Texas Asaphomyian Tabanid Fly	I	U.S.A.
Brennania belkini	Belkin's Dune Tabanid Fly	E	Mexico
Merycomyia brunnea	Brown Merycomyian Tabanid Fly	I	U.S.A.
Stonemyia volutina	Volutine Stoneyian Tabanid Fly	Ex	[U.S.A.]
Family Acroceridae			
Eulonchus marialiciae	Mary Alice's Small-headed Fly	I	U.S.A.
Family Asilidae			
Cophura hurdi	Antioch Robberfly	I	U.S.A.
Efferia antiochi	Antioch Robberfly	I	U.S.A.
Metapogon hurdi	Hurd's Robberfly	I	U.S.A.
Family Apiocertidae			
Raphiomydas triochilus	Valley Mydas Fly	I	U.S.A.
Family Empididae			
Chersodromia hawaiiensis	Hawaiian Dance Fly	I	Hawaii
Family Dolichopodidae			
Campsicnemus mirabilis		Ex	[Hawaii]
Family Syrphidae			
Mixogaster delongi	Delong's Flower Fly	I	U.S.A.

Family Asteiidae			
Bryania bipunctata	Nihoa Two-spotted Asterid Fly	I	Hawaii
Family Drosophilidae			
Drosophila lanaiensis		Ex	[Hawaii]
Family Ephydridae			
Paracoenia calida	Wilber Springs Shore Fly	I	U.S.A.
Order TRICHOPTERA			
Family Rhyacophilidae			
Rhyacophila alexandra	Alexander's Caddisfly	I	U.S.A.
Rhyacophila amabilis	Castle Lake Caddisfly	Ex	[U.S.A.]
Rhyacophila colonus	Obrien Caddisfly	I	U.S.A.
Rhyacophila fenderi	Fender's Caddisfly	I	U.S.A.
Rhyacophila haddocki	Haddock's Caddisfly	I	U.S.A.
Rhyacophila lineata	Castle Crags Caddisfly	I	U.S.A.
Rhyacophila mosana	Bilobed Caddisfly	I	U.S.A.
Rhyacophila spinata	Spiny Caddisfly	I	U.S.A.
Rhyacophila unipunctata	One-spot Caddisfly	I	U.S.A.
Family Glossosomatidae			
Agapetus artesus	Artesian Caddisfly	I	U.S.A.
Agapetus denningi	Denning's Caddisfly	I	U.S.A.
Agapetus medicus	Arkansas Caddisfly	I	U.S.A.
Protoptila arca	San Marcos Caddisfly	I	U.S.A.
Family Hydrotilidae			
Hydroptila decia	Knoxville Micro Caddisfly	I	U.S.A.
Neotrichia kitae	Kite's Micro Caddisfly	I	U.S.A.
Ochrotrichia alsea	Alsea Micro Caddisfly	I	U.S.A.
Ochrotrichia contorta	Contorted Micro Caddisfly	I	U.S.A.
Ochrotrichia phenosa	Deschutes Micro Caddisfly	I	U.S.A.
Ochrotrichia provosti	Provost's Micro Caddisfly	I	U.S.A.
Ochrotrichia vertreesi	Vertree's Micro Caddisfly	I	U.S.A.
Oxyethira florida	Florida Micro Caddisfly	I	U.S.A.

Family Philopotamidae			
Apatania tavala	Cascades Caddisfly	I	U.S.A.
Cryptochia excella	Kings Canyon Caddisfly	I	U.S.A.
Cryptochia neosa	Blue Mountains Caddisfly	I	U.S.A.
Dolophilodes oregona	Oregon Caddisfly	I	U.S.A.
Ecclisomyia bilera	King's Creek Caddisfly	I	U.S.A.
Farula davisi	Green Springs Mountain Caddisfly	I	U.S.A.
Farula jewetti	Mount Hood Caddisfly	I	U.S.A.
Farula reaperi	Tombstone Prairie Caddisfly	I	U.S.A.
Glyphopsyche missouri	Missouri Caddisfly	I	U.S.A.
Limnephilus alconura	Klamath Caddisfly	I	U.S.A.
Limnephilus atercus	Fort Dick Caddisfly	I	U.S.A.
Neothramma andersoni	Colombian Gorge Caddisfly	I	U.S.A.
Oligophlebodes mostbento	Tombstone Prairie Oligophlebodes	I	U.S.A.
Philocasca oron	Clatsop Caddisfly	I	U.S.A.
Triaenodes tridonata	Three-tooth Caddisfly	Ex	[U.S.A.]
Family Stenopsychidae			
Stenopsychodes lineata		I	Tasmania
Family Polycentropodidae			
Tasmanoplegas spilota		I	Tasmania
Family Limnephilidae			
Archaeophylax vernalis		I	Tasmania
Family Lepidostomatidae			
Lepidostoma fischeri	Fischer's Caddisfly	I	U.S.A.
Lepidostoma goedeni	Goeden's Caddisfly	I	U.S.A.
Family Kokiriidae			
Taskiria mccubbini		I	Tasmania
Taskropsyche lacustris		I	Tasmania
Family Plectrotarsidae			
Nanoplectrus truchanasi		I	Tasmania
Family Sericostomatidae			
Agarodes ziczac	Zigzag Blackwater Caddisfly	I	U.S.A.

Species	Common name	Status	Range
Family Odontoceridae			
Psilotreta hansoni		I	U.S.A.
Family Philorheithridae			
Ramiheithrus kocinus		I	Tasmania
Family Leptoceridae			
Ceraclea floridana	Florida Longhorn Caddisfly	I	U.S.A.
Ceraclea vertreesi	Vertree's Caddisfly	I	U.S.A.
Oecetis parva	Little Longhorn Caddisfly	I	U.S.A.
Triaenodes phalacris	Athens Caddisfly	Ex	[U.S.A.]
Westriplectes pedderensis		I	Tasmania
Order LEPIDOPTERA			
Family Hepialidae			
Leto venus	Silver Spotted Ghost Moth	V	South Africa
Zelotypia stacyi	Bent Wing Swift Moth	V	Australia
Family Nepticulidae			
Ectodemia castaneae	American Chestnut Moth	Ex?	[U.S.A.]
Ectodemia phleophaga	Phleophagan Chestnut Moth	Ex?	[U.S.A.]
Family Tischeriidae			
Tischeria perplexa	Chestnut Clearwing Moth	Ex?	[U.S.A.]
Family Gracillariidae			
Petrochroa neckerensis	Necker Leaf-miner Moth	I	Hawaii
Phildoria wilkesiella		E	Hawaii
Family Coleophoridae			
Coleophora leucochrysella		Ex?	[U.S.A.]
Family Gelechiidae			
Kiwaia jeanae		V	New Zealand
Family Carposinidae			
Heterocrossa viridis	Green Carposinid Moth	I	Hawaii
Family Argyresthiidae			
Argyresthia castaneela	Chestnut Ermine Moth	Ex?	[U.S.A.]

Family Sesiidae			
Synanthedon castaneae	Chestnut Clearwing Moth	I	U.S.A.
Family Tortricidae			
Grapholitha edwardsiana	San Francisco Tree Lupine	R	U.S.A.
Spheterista oheoheana	Ohe Ohe Leaf-roller Moth	I	Hawaii
Spheterista pterotropiana	Green-banded Ohe Ohe Leaf-roller Moth	I	Hawaii
Spheterista reynoldsiana	Wallupe Leaf-roller Moth	I	Hawaii
Family Cochylidae			
Carolella busckana	Busk's Gall Moth	I	U.S.A.
Family Hesperiidae			
Antipodia chaostola leucophaea		I	Tasmania
Carterocephalus palaemon	Chequered Skipper	V	Central & North Europe
Dalla octomaculata	Eight Spotted Skipper	R	Costa Rica, Panama
Epargyreus antaeus		R	Jamaica
Epargyreus spana		R	Dominican Republic
Euscheman rafflesia	Skipper	K	Australia
Hesperia dacotae	Dakota Skipper	E	U.S.A., Canada
Hesperia pawnee montana	Pawnee Montane Skipper	E	U.S.A.
Hesperilla mastersi marakupa		I	Tasmania
Kedestes barerae bunta	Barber's Ranger	V	South Africa
Kedestes chaca		V	South Africa
Metisella syrinx	Bamboo Sylph	V	South Africa
Oreisplanus munionga larana		I	Tasmania
Panoquina errans	Wandering Skipper	V	U.S.A., Mexico
Panoquina panoquinoides errans	Salt Marsh Skipper	V	U.S.A., Mexico
Problema buienta	Rare Skipper	I	U.S.A.
Pseudocopaeodes eunus eunus	Wandering Skipper	I	U.S.A.
Syrichtus cribrellum	Spinose Skipper	I	Romania, Southern U.S.S.R.
Syrichtus tessellum	Tessellated Skipper	K	Balkans, Southern U.S.S.R., Iran
Tsitana dicksoni	Dickson's Sylph	V	South Africa
Family Megathymidae			
Stallingsia maculosus	Maculated Manfreda Skipper	I	U.S.A.

Family Papilionidae

Species	Common name	Status	Distribution
Archon apollinaris		R	Turkey
Atrophaneura atropos		I	Philippines
Atrophaneura jophon	Sri Lankan Rose	V	Sri Lanka
Atrophaneura luchti		R	Java
Atrophaneura palu		K	Sulawesi
Atrophaneura schadenbergi		V	Philippines
Baronia brevicornis	Short-horned Baronia	R	Mexico
Battus zetides	Zetides Swallowtail	V	Hispaniola
Bhutanitis ludlowi	Ludlow's Bhutan Swallowtail	K	Bhutan
Bhutanitis mansfieldi	Mansfield's Three-tailed Swallowtail	R	China
Bhutanitis thaidina	Chinese Three-tailed Swallowtail	R	China
Eurytides iphitas	Yellow Kite Swallowtail	V	Brazil
Eurytides lysithous harrisianus	Harris' Mimic Swallowtail	E	Brazil
Eurytides marcellinus	Jamaican Kite	V	Jamaica
Graphium alebion chungianus		R	Taiwan
Graphium antiphates ceylonicus	Sri Lankan Five-bar Swordtail	V	Sri Lanka
Graphium aurivilliusi		K	Zaire
Graphium epaminondas	Andamans Swordtail	K	Andaman Is
Graphium idaeoides		R	Philippines
Graphium levassori		V	Comoro Is
Graphium meeki	Meek's Graphium	R	Bougainville, Solomon Is
Graphium megaera		I	Philippines
Graphium mendana		R	Bougainville, Solomon Is
Graphium procles		I	Sabah
Graphium sandawanum		V	Philippines
Graphium stresemanni		R	Moluccas
Luehdorfia chinensis	Chinese Luehdorfia	K	China
Luehdorfia japonica	Japanese Luehdorfia	I	Japan, Taiwan
Ornithoptera aesacus		I	Moluccas
Ornithoptera alexandrae	Queen Alexandra's Birdwing	E	Papua New Guinea
Ornithoptera chimaera	Chimaera Birdwing	I	New Guinea
Ornithoptera croesus		V	Moluccas
Ornithoptera meridionalis		V	New Guinea
Ornithoptera paradisea	Paradise Birdwing	I	New Guinea
Ornithoptera rothschildi	Rothschild's Birdwing	I	Irian Jaya
Ornithoptera tithonus		K	Irian Jaya
Papilio acheron		R	Sabah, Sarawak
Papilio antimachus	African Giant Swallowtail	R	Central & West Africa

Papilio aristodemus ponceanus	Schaus' Swallowtail	E	U.S.A.
Papilio aristophontes		I	Comoro Is
Papilio aristor	Scarce Haitian Swallowtail	I	Hispaniola
Papilio benguetanus		V	Philippines
Papilio caiguanabus	Poey's Black Swallowtail	I	Cuba
Papilio carolinensis		V	Philippines
Papilio chikae		E	Philippines
Papilio desmondi teita	Taita Blue-banded Papilio	E	Kenya
Papilio esperanza		V	Mexico
Papilio garleppi		K	South America
Papilio grosesmithi		R	Madagascar
Papilio himeros		V	Argentina, Brazil
Papilio homerus	Homerus Swallowtail	E	Jamaica
Papilio hospiton	Corsican Swallowtail	E	Corsica, Sardinia
Papilio jordani	Jordan's Swallowtail	R	Sulawesi
Papilio leucotaenia	Cream-banded Swallowtail	V	Burundi, Rwanda, Uganda
Papilio mangoura		R	Madagascar
Papilio manlius		I	Mauritius
Papilio maraho		V	Taiwan
Papilio maroni		K	French Guiana
Papilio moerneri		V	Bismarck Arch.
Papilio morondavana	Madagascan Emperor Swallowtail	V	Madagascar
Papilio neumoegeni		V	Lesser Sunda Is
Papilio osmana		V	Philippines
Papilio phorbanta	Papillon La Pature	V	Reunion
Papilio phorbanta nana		Ex	[Seychelles]
Papilio sjoestedti	Kilimanjaro Swallowtail	R	Tanzania
Papilio toboroi		R	Bougainville, Solomon Is
Papilio weymeri		R	Bismarck Arch.
Parides ascanius	Fluminense Swallowtail	V	Brazil
Parides burchellanus		V	Brazil
Parides coelus		K	French Guiana
Parides hahneli	Hahnel's Amazonian Swallowtail	R	Brazil
Parides klagesi		K	Venezuela
Parides pizarro		K	Brazil
Parides steinbachi		K	Bolivia
Parnassius apollo	Apollo	R	Europe & U.S.S.R. to China
Parnassius apollo vinningensis		E	F.R.G.
Parnassius autocrator		R	Afghanistan, Tadzhikistan

Parnassius clodius shepardii	Shepard's Clodius Parnassian	I	U.S.A.
Parnassius clodius strohbeeni	Strohbeen's Clodius Parnassian	Ex	[U.S.A.]
Teinopalpus aureus	Golden Kaiser-I-Hind	K	China
Teinopalpus imperialis	Kaiser-I-Hind	R	India to China
Troides aeacus kaguya		E	Taiwan
Troides andromache		I	Sabah, Sarawak
Troides dohertyi	Talaud Black Birdwing	V	Sulawesi
Troides prattorum		I	Moluccas
Family Pieridae			
Artogeia virginiensis	West Virginia White	I	Canada, U.S.A.
Belenois orgygia		E	South Africa
Euchloe hyantis andrewsi	Andrew's Marble Butterfly	I	U.S.A.
Mylothris carcassoni		R	Zimbabwe
Pieris krueperi devta		R	India
Family Lycaenidae			
Alaena margaritacea		V	South Africa
Aloeides caledoni		V	South Africa
Aloeides dentatis		R	South Africa
Aloeides egerides		V	South Africa
Aloeides lutescens		V	South Africa
Argyrocupha malagrida malagrida	Lion's Head Copper	V	South Africa
Argyrocupha malagrida paarlensis	Lion's Head Copper	V	South Africa
Callophrys mossii bayensis	San Bruno Elfin	E	U.S.A.
Capys penningtoni		E	South Africa
Chrysoritis cotrelli		I	South Africa
Chrysoritis oreas	Drakensburg Copper	I	South Africa
Chrysoritis zeuxo		I	South Africa
Cyclyrius mandersi		I	Mauritius
Deloneura immaculata		Ex?	[South Africa]
Deloneura millari millari	Millar's Buff	V	South Africa
Deudorix penningtoni		V	South Africa
Deudorix vansoni		V	South Africa
Durbania limbata		V	South Africa
Erikssonia acraeina		R	South Africa
Eumaeus atala florida	Florida Atala Hairstreak	V	U.S.A.
Everes comyntas texanus	Texas Tailed Blue	Ex	[U.S.A.]
Glaucopsyche lygdamus palosverdesensi	Palos Verdes Blue	Ex?	[U.S.A.]

Glaucopsyche xerces	Xerces Blue	Ex	[U.S.A.]
Hemiargus thomasi bethune-bakeri	Miami Blue Butterfly	I	U.S.A.
Icaricia icarioides missionensis	Mission Blue	E	U.S.A.
Icaricia icarioides moroensis	Moro Blue Bay Blue	I	U.S.A.
Icaricia icarioides pheres	Pheres Blue	I	U.S.A.
Lepidochrysops ariadne		E	South Africa
Lepidochrysops bacchus	Wineland Blue	V	South Africa
Lepidochrysops hypopolia		Ex?	[South Africa]
Lepidochrysops loewensteini		V	South Africa
Lepidochrysops lotana		E	South Africa
Lepidochrysops methymna dicksoni		E	South Africa
Lepidochrysops titei		V	South Africa
Lycaeides argyrognomon lotis	Lotis Blue	E	U.S.A.
Lycaeides melissa samuelis	Karner Blue	I	U.S.A.
Lycaena dispar	Large Copper	E	Northern Europe
Lycaena dorcas claytoni	Clayton's Copper	I	U.S.A.
Lycaena hermes	Hermes Copper	I	U.S.A., Mexico
Maculinea alcon	Alcon Large Blue	V	Europe, U.S.S.R.
Maculinea arion	Large Blue	V	Europe, U.S.S.R.
Maculinea arionides	Greater Large Blue	V	China, Japan, U.S.S.R.
Maculinea arionides matsumara	Greater Large Blue	V	China, Japan, U.S.S.R.
Maculinea nausithous	Dusky Large Blue	E	Europe, U.S.S.R.
Maculinea rebeli	Rebel's Large Blue	V	South & Central Europe
Maculinea teleius	Scarce Large Blue	E	Europe & Northern Asia
Maculinea teleius burdigalensis	Scarce Large Blue	E	France
Notarthrinus binghami		R	India
Oreolyce dohertyi	Naga Hedge Blue	R	India
Ornipholidotos peucetia penningtoni	White Mimic	I	Mozambique, South Africa
Oxychaeta dicksoni	Dickson's Copper	E	South Africa
Panchala ganesa loomisi	Tailless Blue	E	Japan
Philotiella speciosa bohartorum	Bohart's Blue	I	U.S.A.
Plebejus emigdionis	San Emigdio Blue	I	U.S.A.
Plebejus icarioides missionensis	Mission Blue	E	U.S.A.
Plebicula golgus	Nevada Blue	E	Spain
Poecilmitis adonis		V	South Africa
Poecilmitis aureus		I	South Africa
Poecilmitis endymion		V	South Africa
Poecilmitis lyncurium	Tsomo River Copper	V	South Africa

Poecilmitis nigricans	Blue Jewel Copper	V	South Africa
Poecilmitis rileyi		V	South Africa
Pseudalmenus chlorinda chlorinda		I	Tasmania
Pseudalmenus chlorinda conara		I	Tasmania
Pseudiolaus lulua	White Spotted Sapphire	V	South Africa
Shijimiaeoides battoides allyni	El Segundo Blue	E	U.S.A.
Shijimiaeoides battoides comstocki	Comstock's Blue	I	U.S.A.
Shijimiaeoides enoptes smithi	Smith's Blue	E	U.S.A.
Shijimiaeoides langstoni langstoni	Langston's Blue	I	U.S.A.
Shijimiaeoides rita mattonii	Mattoni's Blue	I	U.S.A.
Spindasis collinsi		V	Tanzania
Strymon acis bartrami	Bartram's Hairstreak	I	U.S.A.
Strymon avalona	Avalon Hairstreak	K	U.S.A.
Thestor dicksoni dicksoni	Dickson's Thestor	V	South Africa
Thestor kaplani	Kaplan's Thestor	V	South Africa
Thestor tempe		V	South Africa
Trimenia wallengrenii	Wallengren's Copper	V	South Africa
Uranothauma usambarae		V	Tanzania
Family Libytheidae			
Libythea cinyras		Ex	[Mauritius]
Family Danaidae (or Nymphalidae: Danainae)			
Amauris comorana		R	Comoro Is
Amauris nossima		R	Comoro Is, Madagascar
Amauris pheodon		R	Mauritius
Anetia briarea		R	Cuba, Hispaniola
Anetia cubana		R	Cuba
Anetia jaegeri		R	Hispaniola
Anetia pantheratus		R	Cuba, Hispaniola
Danaus cleophile		K	Hispaniola, Jamaica
Euploea albicosta		R	Irian Jaya
Euploea blossomae		R	Philippines
Euploea caespes		R	Indonesia
Euploea configurata		R	Sulawesi
Euploea cordelia		R	Sulawesi
Euploea dentiplaga		R	Indonesia
Euploea doretta		R	Bismarck Arch.
Euploea eboraci		R	Bismarck Arch.

Euploea eupator		R	Sulawesi
Euploea euphon		R	Mauritius, Reunion, Rodrigues
Euploea gamelia		R	Java
Euploea lacon		R	Bismarck Arch.
Euploea latifasciata		R	Sulawesi
Euploea magou		R	Sulawesi
Euploea martinii		R	Sumatra
Euploea mitra		R	Seychelles
Euploea tobleri		R	Philippines
Euploea tripunctata		R	Irian Jaya
Idea electra		R	Philippines
Idea iasonia		R	Sri Lanka
Idea malabarica		R	India
Idea tambusisiana	Sulawesi Tree Nymph	K	Sulawesi
Ideopsis hewitsonii		R	Irian Jaya
Ideopsis klassika		R	Indonesia
Ideopsis oberthurii		R	Indonesia
Parantica albata		R	Java, Sumatra
Parantica clinias		R	Bismarck Arch.
Parantica crowleyi		R	Borneo
Parantica dannatti		R	Philippines
Parantica davidi		E	Philippines
Parantica garamantis		R	Bougainville, Solomon Is
Parantica kirbyi		K	New Guinea
Parantica kuekenthali		R	Sulawesi
Parantica marcia		R	Irian Jaya
Parantica menadensis		R	Sulawesi
Parantica milagros		R	Philippines
Parantica nilgiriensis		R	India
Parantica philo		R	Indonesia
Parantica phyle		R	Philippines
Parantica pseudomelaneus		R	Java
Parantica pumila		R	New Caledonia
Parantica rotundata		R	Bismarck Arch.
Parantica schoenigi		R	Philippines
Parantica sulewattan		R	Sulawesi
Parantica taprobana		R	Sri Lanka
Parantica tityoides		R	Sumatra
Parantica toxopei		R	Sulawesi

Parantica wegneri		R	Indonesia
Parantica weiskei		R	New Guinea
Protoploea apatela		R	New Guinea
Tiradelphe schneideri		R	Solomon Is
Tirumala euploeomorpha		R	Solomon Is
Tirumala gautama		R	Indochina, China, Malaysia
Family Satyridae (or Nymphalidae: Satyrinae)			
Coenonympha oedippus	False Ringlet	E	Europe & Northern Asia
Erebia annada annada		R	Bhutan, India
Erebia christi	Raetzer's Ringlet	V	Italy, Switzerland
Erebia gorgone	Gavarnie Ringlet	I	France
Erebia narasingha narasingha		R	India
Erebia ottomana	Ottoman Brassy Ringlet	R	Southern Europe
Erebia scipio	Larche Ringlet	R	France, Italy
Erebia sthennyo	False Dewy Ringlet	R	France, Spain
Erebia sudetica	Sudeten Ringlet	V	Europe
Lethe distans	Scarce Red Forester	R	Burma, India
Lethe dura gammiei		R	Bhutan, India
Lethe europa tamuna		R	India
Lethe gemina gafuri		R	India
Lethe margaritae		R	Bhutan, India
Lethe ocellata lyncus		R	Bhutan, India
Lethe ramadeva		R	Bhutan, Burma, India
Lethe satyavati		R	India
Pararge menava maeroides		R	India
Stygionympha dicksoni	Dickson's Brown	V	South Africa
Ypthima dohertyi persimilis		R	Burma, India
Family Nymphalidae (or Nymphalidae: Nymphalinae)			
Anaea floridalis	Florida Leafwing	I	U.S.A.
Antanartia borbonica		I	Madagascar, Mauritius, Reunion
Antanartia borbonica mauritiana		E	Mauritius
Apaturopsis kilusa		R	Madagascar
Apaturopsis pauliani		R	Madagascar
Apodemia mormo langei	Lange's Metalmark	E	U.S.A.
Boloria acrocnema	Uncompahgre Fritillary Butterfly	V	U.S.A.
Cercyonis sthenele sthenele	Sthenele Wood Nymph	Ex	[U.S.A.]
Charaxes cowani		R	Madagascar

Charaxes druceanus entabeni	Silver Barred Charaxes	V	South Africa
Charaxes druceanus williamsi		I	Kenya
Charaxes durnfordi nicholi	Chestnut Rajah	R	Burma, India
Charaxes karkloof capensis		V	South Africa
Charaxes marieps		V	South Africa
Charaxes usambarae		V	Tanzania
Charaxes xiphares desmondi		V	Kenya
Charaxes xiphares xiphares	Western Forest Emperor	V	South Africa
Cymothoe alcimeda alcimeda	Battling Glider	V	South Africa
Cymothoe amaniensis		V	Tanzania
Cymothoe aurivillii		R	Tanzania
Cymothoe magambae		V	Tanzania
Cymothoe melanjae		R	Malawi
Cymothoe teita		V	Kenya
Doleschallia bisaltide andamana	Andaman Leafwing	R	Andaman Is
Euphydryas editha bayensis	Bay Checkerspot Butterfly	E	U.S.A.
Euphydryas editha monoensis	Mono Checkerspot Butterfly	I	U.S.A.
Euryphura achlys	Mottled Green	I	East & South Africa
Euthalia malapana		Ex	[Taiwan]
Euxanthe madagascariensis		R	Madagascar
Fabriciana elisa	Corsican Fritillary	V	France, Italy
Heliconius charltonius peruvianus		V	Ecuador, Peru
Heliconius nattereri	Natterer's Longwing	E	Brazil
Heteronympha cordace comptena		I	Tasmania
Hypodryas maturna	Scarce Fritillary	E	Europe
Hypolimnas antevorta		V	Tanzania
Hypolimnas dubius drucei		I	Comoro Is, Madagascar, Mauritius
Neptis decaryi		R	Madagascar
Neptis manasa	Pale Hockeysticker Sailer	R	China, India, Sikkim
Neptis metella gratilla		R	Madagascar
Neptis nycteas		R	Sikkim
Neptis sankara nar		R	Andaman Is
Neptis sextilla		I	Madagascar
Phalanta philiberti		E	Seychelles
Phyciodes batesi	Tawny Crescent Butterfly	I	U.S.A.
Salamis angustina	Salamis Retrecie	I	Madagascar, Mauritius
Salamis angustina angustina	Salamis Retrecie	I	Madagascar, Reunion
Salamis angustina vinsoni		Ex	[Mauritius]
Sasakia charonda		I	Japan, Taiwan

Satyrodes eurydice fumosa	Smokey Eyed Brown Butterfly	I	U.S.A.
Smerina manoro		R	Madagascar
Speyeria adiaste atossa	Atossa	Ex	[U.S.A.]
Speyeria callippe callippe	Callippe Silverspot	I	U.S.A.
Speyeria hydaspe conquista	Silverspot	I	U.S.A.
Speyeria idalia	Regal Fritillary	I	Canada, U.S.A.
Speyeria nokomis caerulescens	Blue Silverspot	I	U.S.A.
Speyeria nokomis nokomis	Great Basin Silverspot	I	U.S.A.
Speyeria zerene behrensii	Behren's Silverspot	I	U.S.A.
Speyeria zerene hippolyta	Oregon Silverspot	V	U.S.A.
Speyeria zerene myrtleae	Myrtle's Fritillary	R	U.S.A.
Family Acraeidae (or Nymphalidae: Acraeinae)			
Acraea hova		R	Madagascar
Acraea sambavae		R	Madagascar
Family Pyralidae			
Hedylepta (14 species)	Hedyleptan Moths	T*	Hawaii
Kupea electilis		V	New Zealand
Margaronia cyanomichla	Blue Margaronian	I	Hawaii
Margaronia exaula	Green Margaronian	I	Hawaii
Oeoblia dryadopa	Ohenaupaka Oeobian Moth	I	Hawaii
Family Geometridae			
Acalyphes philorites		I	Tasmania
Dirce aesiodora		I	Tasmania
Dirce lunaris		I	Tasmania
Dirce oriplancta		I	Tasmania
Dirce solaris		I	Tasmania
Fletcherana ioxantha	Ioxantha Looper Moth	I	Hawaii
Gnophos obscurata		K	Austria
Scotorythra megalophylla	Kona Giant Looper Moth	Ex?	[Hawaii]
Scotorythra nesiotes	Ko'olau Giant Looper Moth	Ex?	[Hawaii]
Scotorythra paratactis	Hawaiian Hopseed Looper Moth	Ex?	[Hawaii]
Tritocleis microphylla	Ola'a Peppered Looper Moth	Ex?	[Hawaii]
Family Lasiocampidae			
Eriogaster catax		E	Austria, Belgium, F.R.G., Hungary
Phyllodesma ilicifolia	Small Lappet Moth	V	Central & North Europe to Japan

Species	Common name	Status	Distribution
Family Saturniidae			
Graellsia isabelae	Spanish Moon Moth	V	France, Spain
Saturnia pyri	Great Peacock Moth	E	Austria, Czechoslovakia, F.R.G.
Family Sphingidae			
Celerio wilsoni perkinsi		E	Hawaii
Euproserpinus euterpe	Kern Primrose Sphinx Moth	V	U.S.A.
Euproserpinus wiesti	Prairie Sphinx Moth	E	U.S.A.
Hyles hippophaes		V	Europe & U.S.S.R.
Manduca blackburni	Blackburn's Sphinx Moth	Ex?	[Hawaii]
Proserpinus proserpina		V	Central & South Europe, Middle East
Tinostoma smaragditis	Fabulous Green Sphinx of Kauai	Ex?	[Hawaii]
Family Noctuidae			
Acronicta albarufa	Albarufan Dagger Moth	I	Canada, U.S.A.
Agrotis crinigera	Poko Noctuid Moth	Ex?	[Hawaii]
Agrotis fasciata	Midway Noctuid Moth	Ex	[Hawaii]
Agrotis kerri	Kerr's Noctuid Moth	Ex?	[Hawaii]
Agrotis laysanensis	Laysan Noctuid Moth	Ex	[Hawaii]
Agrotis photophila		Ex	[Hawaii]
Agrotis procellaris	Procellaris grotis Noctuid Moth	Ex	[Hawaii]
Catocala marmorata	Marbled Underwing Moth	I	U.S.A.
Catocala pretiosa	Precious Underwing Moth	I	U.S.A.
Erythroecia hebardi	Hebard's Noctuid Moth	I	U.S.A.
Helicoverpa confusa	Confused Moth	Ex?	[Hawaii]
Helicoverpa minuta	Minute Noctuid Moth	Ex	[Hawaii]
Hydraecia petasitis		E	Austria, F.R.G.
Hypena laysanensis	Laysan Dropseed Noctuid Moth	Ex	[Hawaii]
Hypena neweili	Hilo Noctuid Moth	Ex?	[Hawaii]
Hypena plagiota	Lovegrass Noctuid Moth	Ex?	[Hawaii]
Hypena senicula	Kaholuamano Noctuid Moth	Ex?	[Hawaii]
Lithophane lemmeri	Lemmer's Noctuid Moth	I	U.S.A.
Peridroma porphyrea		Ex	[Hawaii]
Pyreferra ceromatica	Ceromatic Noctuid Moth	I	Canada, U.S.A.
Order HYMENOPTERA			
Family Eupelmidae			
Eupelmus nihoaensis	Nihoa Eupelmus Wasp	I	Hawaii

Family Bethylidae			
Sclerodermus nihoaensis	Nihoa Sclerodermus Wasp	I	Hawaii
Family Mutillidae			
Myrmosula pacifica	Antioch Mutillid Wasp	I	U.S.A.
Family Formicidae			
Anergates atratulus		I	F.R.G., Switzerland, U.K.
Aneuretus simoni	Sri Lankan Relict Ant	K	Sri Lanka
Aulacopone relicta	Caucasian Relict Ant	K	Azerbaydzhan
Camponotus aethiops		I	F.R.G.
Camponotus dalmaticus		I	Switzerland
Camponotus fallax		I	F.R.G.
Camponotus universitatis		I	F.R.G., France
Epimyrma groesswaldi		I	Europe
Epimyrma ravouxi	Ravoux's Slavemaker Ant	R	Central & Southern Europe
Formica aquilonia		V	F.R.G.
Formica lugubris		V	F.R.G., Italy
Formica polyctena	European Red Wood Ant	V	F.R.G., Italy
Formica pratensis		V	U.K.
Formica rufa	Red Wood Ant	V	Central Europe
Formica transkaucasica	Black Bog Ant	I	Northern Europe
Formica uralensis		I	F.R.G., Switzerland
Leptothorax goesswaldi	Goesswald's Inquiline Ant	K	Switzerland
Myrmica bibikoffi		I	Switzerland
Myrmica slovaca		I	Switzerland
Nothomyrmecia macrops	Australian Ant	K	Australia
Polyergus rufescens		I	F.R.G.
Family Vespidae			
Odynerus niihauensis	Niihau Vespid Wasp	E	Hawaii
Odynerus soror	Soror Vespid Wasp	E	Hawaii
Family Sphecidae			
Deinomimesa hawaiiensis	Hawaiian Sphecid Wasp	E	Hawaii
Deinomimesa punae	Puna Sphecid Wasp	E	Hawaii
Ectemnius curtipes	Short-foot Sphecid Wasp	E	Hawaii
Ectemnius fulvicrus	Brown Cross Sphecid Wasp	E	Hawaii
Ectemnius giffardi	Giffard's Sphecid Wasp	E	Hawaii

Ectemnius haleakalae	Haleakala Sphecid Wasp	E	Hawaii
Ectemnius nesocrabo bidecoratus	Bidecoratus Sphecid Wasp	I	Hawaii
Eucerceris ruficeps	Redheaded Sphecid Wasp	I	U.S.A.
Nesomimesa kauaiensis	Kauai Sphecid Wasp	E	Hawaii
Nesomimesa perkins		E	Hawaii
Nesomimesa sciopteryx	Shade-winged Sphecid Wasp	E	Hawaii
Philanthus nasalis	Antioch Sphecid Wasp	I	U.S.A.
Family Colletidae			
Nesoprosopis (57 species)	Yellow-faced Bee	T	Hawaii
Family Andrenidae			
Perdita hirticeps luteocincta	Yellow Banded Andrenid Bee	I	U.S.A.
Perdita scitula antiochensis	Antioch Andrenid Bee	I	U.S.A.
Family Megachilidae			
Chalicodoma pluto	Wallace's Giant Bee	K	Moluccas
CLASS ONYCHOPHORA			
Order ONYCHOPHORA			
Family Peripatidae	Peripatus (10 genera)	V	Equatorial Tropics
Family Peripatopsidae	Peripatus (12 genera)	V	Southern Hemisphere
Dendy sp. (3 species)		I	Tasmania
Euperipatoides sp.nr. leuckarti		I	Tasmania
Ooperipatellus insignis		I	Tasmania

Phylum ECHINODERMATA

CLASS ECHINOIDA			
Order ECHINOIDA			
Family Echinidae			
Echinus esculentus	European Edible Sea Urchin	K	North-east Atlantic
Paracentrotus lividus	Purple Urchin	CT	North-east Atlantic, Mediterranean

INDEX